Developing
**literacy**
Skills

# Through History

## KEY STAGE 2: Y3–4

# CHRISTINE MOORCROFT

HOPSCOTCH
EDUCATIONAL PUBLISHING

# ✦ Contents ✦

Published by Hopscotch Educational Publishing Ltd,
29 Waterloo Place, Leamington Spa CV32 5LA
(Tel: 01926 744227)

© 2001 Hopscotch Educational Publishing

Written by Christine Moorcroft
Series design by Blade Communications
Illustrated by David Burroughs
Cover illustrated by Susan Hutchinson
Printed by Clintplan, Southam

Christine Moorcroft hereby asserts her moral right to be identified
as the author of this work in accordance with the Copyright,
Designs and Patents Act, 1988.

ISBN 1-902239-76-8

# Introduction

 ## ABOUT THE SERIES

*Developing Literacy Skills Through History* is a series of books aimed at developing key literacy skills using a range of written genres based on a history theme, from Key Stage 1 (P1–3) through to Key Stage 2 (P4–7).

The series offers a structured approach which provides detailed lesson plans to teach specific literacy and history skills. A unique feature of the series is the provision of differentiated photocopiable activities aimed at considerably reducing teacher preparation time. Suggestions for follow-up activities for both literacy and history ensure maximum use of this resource.

## ABOUT THIS BOOK

This book is for teachers of children at Key Stage 2, Years 3–4 and Scottish levels P4–5. It aims to:

◆ develop children's literacy and history skills through exposure to and experience of a wide range of stimulating texts with supporting differentiated activities which are both diversified and challenging
◆ support teachers by providing practical teaching methods based on whole-class, group, paired and individual teaching
◆ encourage enjoyment and curiosity as well as develop skills of interpretation and response.

## CHAPTER CONTENT

 ### Literacy objectives

This outlines the aims for the literacy activities suggested in the lesson plan.

 ### History objectives

This outlines the history learning objectives that relate to the lesson plan.

 ### Resources

This lists the different resources that the teacher needs to teach the lesson.

 ### Starting point: Whole class

This provides ideas for introducing the activity and may include key questions to ask the children.

 ### Using the photocopiable text

This explains how to use the provided text extract with the children as a shared reading activity and introduction to the group work. It may also be used by groups during the group work.

 ### Group activities

This explains how to use each sheet as well as providing guidance on the type of child who will benefit most from each sheet.

 ### Plenary session

This suggests ideas for whole-class sessions to discuss the learning outcomes and follow-up work.

 ### Follow-up ideas for literacy

This contains suggestions for further literacy activities related to the lesson plan, which can be carried out at another time.

 ### Follow-up ideas for history

This contains suggestions for further history activities which might be carried out at another time or during a designated history lesson.

# People on the move

## Literacy objectives

- To make clear notes using abbreviations and a key. (Y3, T2: T17)
- To be able to fill out notes to write connected prose. (Y4, T2: T22)

## History objectives

(Units 6A, 6B or 6C)
- To relate own experience to the concept of settlement.
- To recognise that people have been moving between different areas for a long time, and that some reasons for moving were the same many years ago as today.
- To recognise that communities are made up of people from different places, backgrounds and cultures.

## Resources

- Local maps and maps of the world and the United Kingdom.
- Information books about, and pictures of, immigration and refugees.

## Starting point: Whole class

- Ask the children about their own experiences of moving house and why they moved. (This needs to be handled sensitively since some children might have moved house because of their parents' divorce.) Help the children to find, on appropriate maps, the places from which, and to which, they moved.

- Encourage the children to talk about the differences between their old and new homes and any differences in their way of life. For example, a change of school, how they travel to school and new friends.

- Draw out the reasons why people move house: work; wanting a bigger house or more pleasant surroundings; to 'start a new life' or because of fear (this could be linked with work on refugees or on local problems such as burglary, vandalism, drug-dealing and other crimes).

- Explain what 'immigrant' means and tell the children that some people moved to Britain from other countries to find work. Show them information books and leaflets about immigration and pictures of groups of immigrants travelling. Children from immigrant families might offer to share their experiences or those of their families.

## Using the photocopiable text

- Enlarge the text on page 6 or make a copy for each child. Explain that the text is a girl's notes from a tape-recording made when she interviewed people who had moved from the places where they were born.

- Read the text with the children and ask them to notice from where the people moved. Why did the people move and settle elsewhere?

- Tell the children that to make note-taking quicker, people write shortened forms of words. Draw their attention to the key and point out that some shortened words are so obvious they do not need to be included in the key. Challenge them to find examples of such words in the text. They should notice: 'hol' for 'holiday', 'hosp' for 'hospital', 'N' for 'north', 'S' for 'south' and 'univ' for 'university'. Encourage them to think of abbreviations for other frequently-used words. Point out that symbols can also be used, for example '&' or '+' for 'and', and '–' for 'to'.

- Ask the children to find words and phrases which tell them why the people moved from the places in which they were born. These are the most important words or phrases, the main points of the text. Ask the children to highlight or underline them.

- Invite the children to suggest headings under which the reasons for moving can be grouped, for example work, studies, marriage, to start a new life, fear and so on.

## Group activities

**Using the differentiated activity sheets**

**Activity sheet 1:** This is for children who understand that notes can be written in a short way to save time. They can write sentences and understand how a key is used.

# People on the move

**Activity sheet 2:** This is for children who understand that notes can be written in a short way to save time. They can write up notes as joined prose. They can use a key and are learning to construct keys for themselves.

**Activity sheet 3:** This is for children who understand that notes can be written in a short way to save time. They can write up notes as joined prose and use and construct keys confidently. They are consolidating and developing these skills.

 *Plenary session*

Beginning with the children who completed Activity sheet 1, invite each group of children to share their responses to the tasks on the activity sheets. Encourage the children to share and compare the connected prose they have written based on the notes. Does it contain all the information from the notes? This could also provide an opportunity for comparing the different impressions which can be given by writing about the same facts in different ways.

 *Follow-up ideas for literacy*

✦ Interview people who have moved house, either visitors or people from within the school community. Encourage the children to think of short ways in which to write words to speed up their note-making during the interviews, and to make a key for any abbreviations they might otherwise forget.

✦ Ask the children to use their notes as the basis for a non-chronological report about the reasons why people move away from the places where they were born. The report should have an introduction, paragraphs with subheadings and a conclusion.

✦ Ask the children to name any abbreviations which they often see or use, for example days of the week, measurements, words connected with time and words in addresses and people's titles. Help them to compile a class reference file on a word-processing program (using a table which sorts alphabetically).

✦ Write standard abbreviations on a set of cards and their meanings on a separate set of cards. Play a bingo game in which the players have a set number of abbreviations cards and the caller reads out the full words or names; if they have the abbreviation of the word or name called, they cover it.

✦ Challenge the children to use a dictionary or *Whitaker's Almanac* to find the meanings of other common abbreviations, abbreviations for organisations, and abbreviations for commonly used words and phrases. Ask the children to compile a class abbreviations bank or dictionary (either handwritten or word-processed) to which they can add as necessary. A word-processed dictionary in which each word is entered on a new line of a table would facilitate the arrangement of the words into alphabetical order.

 *Follow-up ideas for history*

✦ Provide information books about refugees who have come to Britain in the past – for example, Jewish refugees from Europe during World War II. Ask the children to collect newspaper articles about refugees arriving in Britain at the present time. Ask them to make notes about the reasons for immigration and where the immigrants come from.

✦ If possible, invite visitors to the class whom the children can question about why they have come to live in the locality from other parts of Britain or from abroad.

✦ Give the children information about particular invaders and settlers in history. Ask them to find out more about them, for example where they came from, the reasons they left their place of birth, where they settled in Britain and why, how long they stayed, whether they all left (and how we know), how their stay affected the people in Britain, and their legacy in Britain, such as buildings, words and place names.

✦ Ask groups of children to look for information about different areas in the list above, make notes (using abbreviations) and contribute to a class book or display about those invaders and settlers.

**Key to some of the abbreviations**

| | | | | | |
|---|---|---|---|---|---|
| **b** | born | **Eng** | England | **fam** | family |
| **f** | father | **fr** | from | **I** | lives (in) |
| **m** | mother | | | | |

**Joan Smith** (teacher) b & I Washington USA. Fam sailed fr Liverpool – America 1850. Emigrants to Australia and America ('New World') in mid 1800s given cheap fares. Plenty of cheap land – start farm. Stayed there.

**Fawzia** (student) b & I near Glasgow. Fam in Glasgow. F came fr Pakistan – London 1970 to study medicine. Works in hosp in Glasgow.

**Liam** (9) b Manchester. I Wales. M b Manchester. F b London (moved to Manchester when married m in 1971). Fam moved to Wales 1987 when f & m gave up work as architects to open art & craft centre in rural area.

**Jenna** (10) b Gateshead. I Enfield. M unemployed. Found work in S of Eng when Jenna was 3. Wants to move back to N to be near fam.

**Laura** (19, student) b Chesterfield. I York. Fam in Chesterfield. Studying physics at Univ of York. Goes home on train at end of every term. Thinks will stay in York to work after univ.

**Jakaki** b Japan 1949. I Cardiff. Came to Eng for hol in 1972. Met Megan in London. Wrote to one another for 4 years. Megan visited J and his fam in Jap and J visited M and her fam in Card. Married 1976.

**Mikhail** (writer) b Russia. I Lake District, Eng. 1969 heard that authorities going to arrest him because of his political work. Left Russia, all belongings and home. Friends helped him to travel – London & found place for him to stay in village in Lake District. Still in same village.

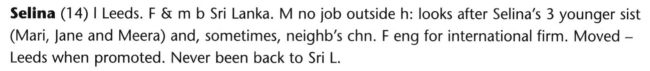

## Making notes

✦ Use the key to help you read the notes.

✦ Rewrite the notes in complete sentences. Write all the
words in full.

---

**Key**

| | | | |
|---|---|---|---|
| **b** | born | **chn** | children |
| **eng** | engineer | **h** | home |
| **f** | father | **l** | lives |
| **m** | mother | **–** | to |

---

**Selina** (14) l Leeds. F & m b Sri Lanka. M no job outside h: looks after Selina's 3 younger sist
(Mari, Jane and Meera) and, sometimes, neighb's chn. F eng for international firm. Moved –
Leeds when promoted. Never been back to Sri L.

_____

_____

_____

_____

_____

_____

_____

_____

©Hopscotch Educational Publishing

# ◆ Making notes ◆

◆ Fill in the gaps in the key.
◆ Use the key to help you read the notes.
◆ Rewrite the notes in complete sentences. Write all the
words in full.

## Key

| b | _____ | **L'pool** | _____ | **'55** | _____ |
|---|---|---|---|---|---|
| **f** | _____ | **m** | mother | **'56** | _____ |
| **gf** | grandfather | **sch** | _____ | **'61** | _____ |
| **gm** | _____ | **–** | to | **'90** | _____ |
| **l** | _____ | **'40** | 1940 | | |

**John** b & l L'pool. Gf b Budapest, Hungary '40. Left sch '55 & worked on f's farm. Wanted other work. – Eng '56 to train as electrician. New car factory in L'pool – work there, met John's gm in L'pool. Married her '61. 6 chn (one was J's f, who married J's m '90).

_____

_____

_____

_____

_____

_____

# ◆ Making notes ◆

◆ Read the notes and make a key to show what the abbreviations mean.

◆ Write the notes in full. Use complete sentences and write all the words in full.

---

**Key**

---

**Scott** (8) b Luton, Eng. l Toronto, Canada. Both gfs & gms, m & f b Lut. 3 chn: Scott, James (6, b Tor) & Laura (4, b Tor). l sml terr house (2 beds) no gard. Decided to emig just aft Scott b for better lifestyle in Can: earn +, bigger house, gard. When gf & gm (f's parents) retired – Tor to be with fam. Oth gf & gm visit ev oth Xmas. Scott & fam – gps in Lut ev oth sum hol.

_____

_____

_____

_____

_____

_____

_____

# Settlers

## Literacy objectives

+ To understand the difference between fact and fiction and to use the terms 'fact', 'fiction' and 'non-fiction' appropriately. (Y3, T1: T16)
+ To notice differences in the style and structure of fiction and non-fiction writing. (Y3, T1: T17)
+ To understand and use the terms 'fact' and 'opinion'. (Y4, T1: T19)

## History objectives

(Unit 6A)

+ To learn about the reason for Boudica's revolt and what happened during it.
+ To learn that there are different interpretations of the revolt.

## Resources

+ Pictures of Colchester, London and St Albans as they were in AD60.
+ Maps showing the routes of Roman roads, and present-day maps showing roads which follow the routes of Roman roads.
+ Pictures of Roman buildings.
+ Pictures of pre-Roman British settlements.

## Starting point: Whole class

+ The children need first to have some knowledge of the Roman invasion and occupation of Britain. They need to know about the lifestyles of the Britons and the Romans.

+ Explain what 'invade' means and ask the children why they think nations invade one another's land. What do they gain from it?

+ Encourage the children to think how they would feel if the place where they live were invaded by another nation, their homes given to people of that nation and they themselves captured and treated as slaves. How would their families react? What might stop them doing anything about the injustice they felt? Then ask them to imagine another point of view – the nation which took them over could provide them with a higher standard of living: good roads, warmer and more comfortable homes, more stylish clothes and a variety of foods they had not seen before.

+ Draw out the different ways in which the Roman rule of Britain could be considered. Was it all bad? Show the children maps of Roman roads where there had been no roads before. Many are still the routes of main roads (for example, Watling Street and Ermine Street). Using pictures, compare Roman buildings, such as baths and villas, with the tribal settlements of the Britons.

## Using the photocopiable text

+ Enlarge the text on page 12 or make a copy for each child. Explain that the text is based on two other, more complicated, texts written for adults. Ask the children if they think the text might be fiction or non-fiction. How can they tell? Point out the headings that help us to find the information we want, and the illustration and caption.

+ Read the text with the children. You may need to spend a little time with them on the Roman names which can be quite difficult to pronounce, let alone read.

+ Discuss the content of the text. Ask them to notice how the language is different from that of fiction. Encourage them to identify the sentences that give information and those that say what people thought or felt. Notice that, unlike in most fiction books, there is no conversation.

+ Reread the first few sentences of the text, a sentence at a time, asking if it gives a fact or opinion. Ask the children how they can tell. Point out that facts can be checked, for example that Camulodunum was a settlement for retired legionaries and that Boudica's husband was Prasutagus. Point out that words such as 'must have' or 'would have' often introduce opinions, but also that some people state their opinions as if they are facts, for example 'Prasutagus thought it best to live in peace with the Romans.' (How can we really know what people thought in AD60 unless they wrote it down?)

## Group activities

**Using the differentiated activity sheets**

**Activity sheet 1:** This is for children who understand that fiction means 'a story' and not events which really happened. They can recognise a fact and know that it is something that really happened or that exists.

# Settlers

**Activity sheet 2:** This is for children who understand that fiction books are about events or people invented by the writer. They know that an opinion is what someone thinks and that it could be right or wrong.

**Activity sheet 3:** This is for children who understand that fiction books are stories written for entertainment and that non-fiction books on history are written to give information and opinions. They can distinguish confidently between fact and fiction and between facts and opinions and are beginning to understand why people might interpret facts in different ways.

## ◆ *Plenary session*

✦ Invite the children who completed Activity sheet 1 to share their responses. Move on to Activity sheet 2 and encourage the children to say how they can tell when a sentence is a fact and when it gives an opinion. Ask the children who completed Activity sheet 3 to read out some of the facts and opinions they found in the text and to say on what evidence some of the opinions were based.

✦ Ask the children why the Iceni and the Trinovantes would have wanted to rebel against the Romans. What facts support their answers?

✦ Encourage the children to suggest reasons why some people might say that Boudica was a cruel revenge-taker and others might say she was a brave fighter for the freedom of her people.

---

###  *Follow-up ideas for literacy*

✦ In which person is the text written, and how can you tell? The children should notice the third person usage of 'she', 'he' and 'they'. Ask them to write a first person account of the revolt, imagining they were there.

✦ Draw attention to the tense in which the text is written, and ask the children to look for examples of verbs in the past tense. Ask them why this tense is used.

✦ Show the children a picture of Boudica and give out cards on which a fact or opinion about her has been written. Challenge the children to sort them into two piles, 'fact' and 'opinion'.

✦ Challenge the children to list, in chronological order, the events of Boudica's revolt and then write a chronological report about it. Use storyboards to help them to split the report into paragraphs.

---

###  *Follow-up ideas for history*

✦ Display pictures of some of the archaeological finds from Colchester (available from the Castle Museum, Colchester, High Street, Colchester CO1 1TJ Tel: 01206 282939). Ask the children what they can learn from them.

✦ Visit a Roman site and a museum containing Roman and British artefacts to find out about the Roman and the British ways of life. Ask the children to compare the two cultures. Ask them to comment on the buildings, the artefacts used in the homes, weapons and armour, and personal adornments.

✦ Invite the children to compare descriptions and images of Boudica and say what impression each source gives of her.

✦ Ask the children to find other versions of Boudica's revolt. What are the similarities and differences between the interpretations?

---

### Camulodunum (Colchester), the Roman capital of Britain

The Roman town of Camulodunum was built as a settlement for retired Roman legionaries. These soldiers were given land there. The idea was probably that they would introduce the Roman way of life to the Britons, so that there would be no difference between the Romans and the Britons. The Britons would then live peacefully alongside the Romans.

### Romans and Trinovantes

The idea did not work because the Roman legionaries' land was taken from the Trinovantes tribe. The Romans captured the Trinovantes and made them slaves. They killed any who rebelled: archaeologists have found the skeletons of Britons of the time with their heads cut off and fixed on to spikes (probably to warn others). Some of the Trinovantes began to live as Romans: they had villas and land. They must have been quite content, unlike those who were slaves.

### The Temple of Claudius

The Roman emperor Claudius died in AD54. The Romans began building a huge temple to him at Camulodunum. It was as if Claudius were a god.

### Boudica (also spelled Boudicca or Boadicea)

Prasutagus, King of the Iceni tribe, thought it best to live in peace with the Romans. Before he died he named his wife, Boudica, their daughters and the new Roman emperor, Nero, as joint rulers of his kingdom. But the Romans treated the Iceni as captives and forced them to surrender. They flogged Boudica and harmed her daughters. She must have wanted revenge. The Romans made young Iceni men join their army; this would have angered the Iceni.

Boudica became Queen of the Iceni of East Anglia in AD60.

### The start of the revolt

Boudica called the Iceni and Trinovantes together. A Roman historian, Dio Cassius, wrote about the speech she made to urge them to fight the Romans. The Romans were born slaves, she said, and had to protect themselves with helmets and breastplates. But the Britons were born free, and were so brave that they could fight without training and with only shields. The Romans had to have good food and clothing, while the Britons could survive on wild plants and water. She led a great horde of Iceni and Trinovantes to Camulodunum. They burned the temple, where the Romans had taken refuge, and killed everyone inside.

# ◆ Fact or opinion ◆

◆ Read the sentences on the spears. Colour the facts blue and the opinions red.

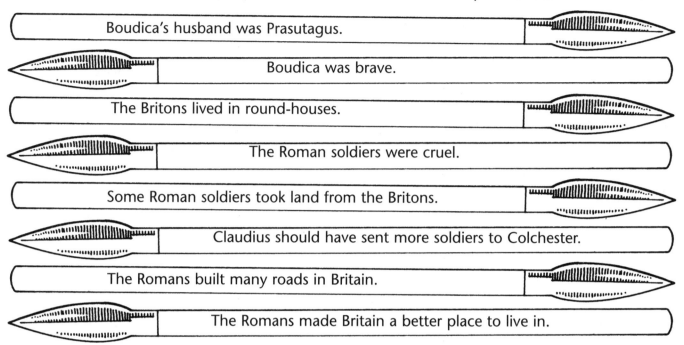

Boudica's husband was Prasutagus.

Boudica was brave.

The Britons lived in round-houses.

The Roman soldiers were cruel.

Some Roman soldiers took land from the Britons.

Claudius should have sent more soldiers to Colchester.

The Romans built many roads in Britain.

The Romans made Britain a better place to live in.

◆ Write the sentences in the correct place on the chart.

| Facts | Opinions |
|---|---|
| Boudica's husband was _____ | Boudica was _____ |

# ✦ Fact or opinion ✦

✦ Read these sentences. Which are facts and which are opinions?

It was a sad day for Britain when the Romans invaded.

In Boudica's time there were many different tribes in Britain.

The Romans called Colchester 'Camulodunum'.

The Iceni were warlike people.

Boudica's tribe was the Iceni.

If there had been a wall around Colchester it would have been safe from Boudica's attack.

It was not fair that Roman soldiers were given land in Colchester.

Claudius was the Roman emperor.

The Romans wanted to show that they were in charge of Colchester and that the Britons had to obey them.

Archaeologists found the head of a statue of Claudius in the River Alde.

The Britons must have knocked the head off the statue and thrown it into the river.

✦ Write the sentences in this chart.

| Facts | Opinions |
|---|---|
|  |  |

## ✦ Fact or opinion ✦

✦ Look for facts and opinions in the text below.
✦ Record your findings on the chart.

The Romans built London in about AD50. They named it Londinium. There had been no settlement there before. By AD60 it was a busy city. The names of many London traders and craftspeople from Roman times have been recorded.

After burning Colchester, Boudica led her army on to London. The Roman general, Suetonius Paulinus, had taken two of his legions to Wales and abandoned the people of London. So it was easy for Boudica's army to charge into the city, kill anyone who got in their way and burn the buildings. Archaeologists found more than a hundred skulls beneath the bed of a stream in London. They thought that the

Britons must have cut off the heads of the Romans and thrown them into the stream. Much later, archaeologists examined the skulls and decided that they probably had nothing to do with Boudica's attack.

After burning London, Boudica and her tribespeople moved on to Verulamium (St Albans). Very few collections of coins have been found on the site of Verulamium. Some historians think this might be because Boudica's horde looted the town so thoroughly that nothing was left. Others think that many of the people there managed to get away with their valuables once they heard that Boudica's army was on its way.

| Facts | Opinions |
|-------|----------|
|       |          |
|       |          |
|       |          |
|       |          |
|       |          |
|       |          |
|       |          |

Chapter 3

# The work of archaeologists

 **Literacy objectives**

- ✦ To record information from texts read. (Y3, T1: T21)
- ✦ To write a simple non-chronological report from known information. (Y3, T1: T22)
- ✦ To write a non-chronological report, including the use of organisational devices. (Y4, T1: T27)

 **History objectives**

(Unit 6B)

- ✦ To place events in a chronological timescale.
- ✦ To learn about what was discovered at Sutton Hoo.
- ✦ To learn what we can find out from objects.
- ✦ To make inferences from archaeological evidence.
- ✦ To make deductions about the person the grave commemorated.

 **Resources**

- ✦ Pictures of archaeologists at work.
- ✦ A picture of the ship outline uncovered at Sutton Hoo.
- ✦ A timeline which includes the seventh century.

 **Starting point: Whole class**

- ✦ Tell the children that they are going to find out about something that happened during the time after the Anglo-Saxons had settled in Britain. Ask them to locate the seventh century on a timeline, and relate it to other periods in history about which they have learned.

- ✦ Ask the children what they know about the work of archaeologists and its purpose. Explain that archaeologists use their knowledge of history to deduce what they have found. Show them pictures of archaeologists at work. Tell them that archaeologists made excavations at Sutton Hoo (show its location on a map). Tell them about the discovery of the ship burial and the story of the mounds.[1]

- ✦ Show the children pictures of the ship outline uncovered at Sutton Hoo. Tell them that although the timber of the ship had rotted away, archaeologists could see the outline of it, and found metal rivets still in place. This told them what the ship must have looked like. Point out that the archaeologists were surprised to find no skeleton in the mound which contained the ship. What do the

children think happened to the body of the person who died?[1] Tell them that this is still a mystery.

- ✦ Explain that the Anglo-Saxons thought that there was an 'after-life' after people died, and they were buried with things which would be useful in the after-life. Tell the children that they are now going to look at pictures of some of those objects.

 **Using the photocopiable text**

- ✦ Enlarge the text on page 18 and mask the captions. Explain that the pictures are drawings made from photographs of the artefacts found in the ship burial at Sutton Hoo. Ask the children to look at each picture in turn and to say what they think each one is and what it might be made of. Encourage them to describe any details they notice.

- ✦ Ask the children how they think each object would have been used, and to explain how they can tell.

- ✦ Give the children a copy of page 18 and read the captions with them. Discuss what we can learn from the artefacts about the lives of rich Anglo-Saxon people and the person who was commemorated by the ship burial.

- ✦ Record the children's ideas on a chart:

| Anglo-Saxon life | | The person commemorated in the ship burial | |
|---|---|---|---|
| The evidence | What it tells us | The evidence | What it tells us |
| | | | |

Tell the children that they are going to use the information from the chart and the shared text to write a report. Discuss the style of report-writing (for example, how it differs from story-writing).

 **Group activities**

**Using the differentiated activity sheets**

**Activity sheet 1:** This is for children who know that a report is a non-fiction text and not a story. They can write sentences and are learning to make notes and to write them as connected prose.

# The work of archaeologists

**Activity sheet 2:** This is for children who understand the difference between fiction and non-fiction. They can make notes and are developing skills in filling out their notes into connected prose. They are learning how to split a report into paragraphs.

**Activity sheet 3:** This is for children who can use the notes they have made to write connected prose, which they can organise into paragraphs with given headings. With support, they can write introductory and concluding paragraphs for a non-chronological report.

 ## Plenary session

✦ Invite the children who completed Activity sheet 1 to share their responses. Move on to Activity sheet 2 and invite the children to share any response which differed from these. Invite the children who completed Activity sheet 3 to read out what they have written.

✦ Ask the children to identify the facts and opinions in their reports. Ask them how they can tell that they are reports and not stories.

---

 ## Follow-up ideas for literacy

✦ Read part of the poem, 'Beowulf', which describes the ship burial of the Danish king Scyld:

*Deep in the ship they laid him down,*
*Their beloved lord, the giver of rings,*
*By the mast in majesty. Great treasures there,*
*Far-gathered trappings were taken and set:*
*No ship in fame more fittingly furnished*
*With weapons of war and battle-armour,*
*With mail-coat and sword; there lay to his hand*
*Countless treasures to go at his side,*
*Voyaging to the distant domains of the sea.*

✦ Talk about the atmosphere of the poem and ask the children to identify the words which give the impression of grandeur. The poem can also be read as a historical source which adds to the evidence uncovered by archaeologists.

✦ Write about the discovery of Sutton Hoo in the form of a letter from an archaeologist to a member of his or her family. Compare the format and style of a letter with that of a report.

✦ Write about the discovery in the form of a newspaper article.

✦ Discuss the audiences of the different forms of writing: whether they consist of one, a small number or many people and whether or not they are known to the writer.

---

 ## Follow-up ideas for history

✦ Give the children some information about the Sutton Hoo burial which could not have been discovered from excavation alone. Talk about the other ways in which historians can find out about the past – for example, from poetry and other writings. Give the children adapted extracts from Anglo-Saxon writings to read.

✦ Ask the children what they would choose to have buried with them, and why. Which things do they think would rot away the most quickly, and what evidence might people in the future find? This could be linked with a scientific investigation.

✦ Few people nowadays have ships. What modern artefact might someone important be buried in? Ask the children to plan a 'car burial'.

✦ Encourage the children to role-play archaeologists of the future excavating the 'car burial' and describing what they have found.

In 1939 an archaeologist named Basil Brown excavated the large mound of earth which covered a buried ship at Sutton Hoo in Suffolk. It had been buried in Anglo-Saxon times, in the seventh century. It was known from written sources from the time, that people like kings and queens were buried in their ships, along with some of their possessions.

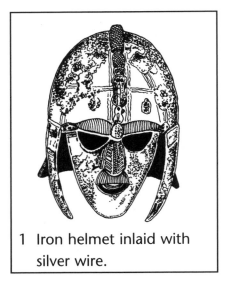

1  Iron helmet inlaid with silver wire.

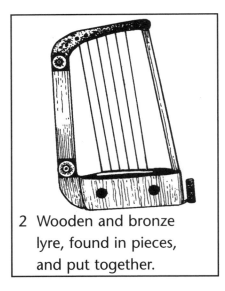

2  Wooden and bronze lyre, found in pieces, and put together.

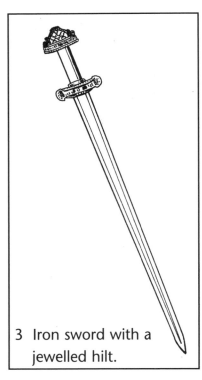

3  Iron sword with a jewelled hilt.

4  This shield was not found in one piece like this. The round part had rotted away, leaving tiny bits of wood and leather clinging to the metal parts. In the centre is the boss. It was more than decoration: it was used to knock the enemy to the ground. The decoration on the left is a serpent; on the right is a raven.

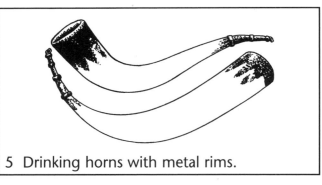

5  Drinking horns with metal rims.

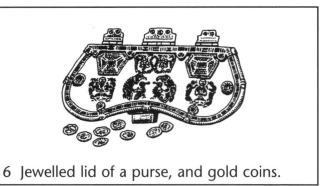

6  Jewelled lid of a purse, and gold coins.

## ◆ Writing a report ◆

✦ Read the Sutton Hoo text again and look at the pictures.
✦ Fill in the gaps in this report. You can use the words in the box.

**Title** _____

### Introduction

In the s_____ century a ship was b_____ at Sutton Hoo.
An arch_____ named Basil Brown found the ship in
19___ It had been covered with a m_____ of earth.

*The introduction says what the report is about.*

### Life in Anglo-Saxon times

The Anglo-Saxons knew how to work with metals like g_____
and i_____ They could make sw_____ and
h_____ from iron, and j_____ and m_____
from gold. Rich people used money to buy things and they carried
it in a p_____

The Anglo-Saxons had musical i_____ such as
l_____ They drank from h_____

*This part says what we can find out about Anglo-Saxon life from the things found at Sutton Hoo.*

### The owner of the ship

The person the ship burial commemorated was a man. We know
this because of the weapons and armour: the sw_____,
sh_____ and h_____ He was rich, because there were
g_____ c_____ and a purse covered with j_____

*This part says what we can find out from the things found there about the person the ship burial commemorated.*

### Conclusion

We can find out about the past from the things which
arch_____ find.

*This part finishes the report. It is a summary of what you have written.*

| | | | | |
|---|---|---|---|---|
| swords | buried | iron | jewellery | seventh |
| horns | instruments | mound | purse | archaeologists |
| lyres | money | 1939 | helmets | |
| shield | coins | gold | jewels | |

## ◆Writing a report◆

✦ Reread the text and look at the pictures.
✦ Fill in the gaps in this report.

### Title

### Introduction
In the s_____ century a ship was b_____ at Sutton Hoo.
An arch_____ named Basil Brown found the ship in 19___
It had been covered with a m_____ of earth.

> The introduction says what the report is about.

### Life in Anglo-Saxon times
The Anglo-Saxons knew how to work with metals like g_____ and i_____
They could make sw_____ and h_____ from iron, and j_____ and m_____ from gold.
Rich people used money to buy things and they carried it in a p_____

The Anglo-Saxons had musical i_____ such as l_____
They drank from h_____

> This part says what we can find out about Anglo-Saxon life from the things found at Sutton Hoo.

### The owner of the ship
The person the ship burial commemorated was a man. We know this  because of the weapons and armour: the sw_____, sh_____ and h_____. He was rich, because there were g_____ c_____ and a purse covered with j_____

> This part says what we can find out from the things found there about the person the ship burial commemorated.

### Conclusion
We can find out about the past from the things which arch_____ find.

> This part finishes the report. It is a summary of what you have written.

**Activity 3**

Name _____

## ◆ Writing a report ◆

✦ What do the pictures in the text tell you about life in England in Anglo-Saxon times?
What do they tell you about the person commemorated by the ship burial at Sutton Hoo?

✦ Write a report about the Sutton Hoo ship.

**Title**

**Introduction**

The introduction says what the report is about.

**Life in Anglo-Saxon times**

This part says what we can find out about Anglo-Saxon life from the things found at Sutton Hoo.

**The owner of the ship**

This part says what we can find out from the things found there about the person the ship burial commemorated.

**Conclusion**

This part finishes the report. It is a summary of what you have written.

# The legacy of the Vikings

 ## Literacy objectives

- To use dictionaries to learn or check the meanings of words. (Y3, T2: W19)
- To understand that some dictionaries provide further information about words (for instance, their origins). (Y3, T3: W15)
- To make alphabetically-ordered texts – use information from other subjects and information books. (Y3, T3: T24)

 ## History objectives

(Unit 6C)
- To learn where the Vikings came from.
- To place the Viking settlement in Britain on a chronological timescale.
- To learn about Viking settlements in Britain.
- To ask and answer questions which can be answered from historical evidence.

 ## Resources

- A dictionary of place names.
- A map of Britain and a map showing Britain and Scandinavia.
- A timeline which includes the ninth, tenth and eleventh centuries.

 ## Starting point: Whole class

- Tell the children that they are going to investigate the names of places in Britain to find out how they are linked to Viking settlements dating from the ninth, tenth and eleventh centuries. Ask them to point to the Viking era on a timeline, and to relate it to other periods in history which they have studied.

- Discuss the meanings of the words 'invade' and 'settle' and tell the children that the date of the first recorded Viking raid, on Lindisfarne in AD793, was written in the Anglo-Saxon Chronicle in about AD892. Explain that, after raiding and trading for about 60 years, the Vikings set up settlements in Britain. Using a map, show them the locations of some of these settlements, in particular York, the centre of the Viking kingdom of Northumbria (north of the Humber) ruled by Eirik Bloodaxe. Show the children where the Vikings came from. Why do they think the Vikings came to Britain (and to other European countries)?

 ## Using the photocopiable text

- Enlarge the text on page 24 or provide the children with copies. Explain that the information has been collected from dictionaries of place names. Show the children a dictionary of place names and point out how it differs from an ordinary dictionary in the extra information it provides.

- Read the text with the children and explain the meanings of words they do not know (or ask them to look them up). Ask them what they notice about the way in which the text is set out. They should notice that it is in alphabetical order. Ask them to name other texts they have read which are in alphabetical order – for example, glossaries, indexes and the class register. Ask them how this helps the reader.

- Point out that each place name is on a new line and in bold type. The Old Norse or Old Scandinavian words are in italic. Introduce the terms 'bold' and 'italic'. Ask the children how the use of bold and italic helps the reader. Challenge them to name other texts in which they have seen these devices.

- Revise the function of a glossary and how it is used. Tell the children that they are going to make a glossary of place names.

 ## Group activities

**Using the differentiated activity sheets**

**Activity sheet 1:** This is for children who know what a glossary is for and can use one with support. They know that the entries in a glossary are arranged in alphabetical order. They can order words alphabetically by the first letter and are learning how to do so by the second letter.

**Activity sheet 2:** This is for children who can use a glossary. They can order words alphabetically by the first and second letters and are learning to do so by considering subsequent letters.

**Activity sheet 3:** This is for children who can use a glossary confidently and can recognise similar-looking words. They can order words alphabetically by considering each letter of the word in turn.

# The legacy of the Vikings

 **Plenary session**

✦ Beginning with the children who completed Activity sheet 1, invite them to read out the list of place names in alphabetical order. Invite them to explain where some of the meanings come from.

✦ Move on to Activity sheet 2 and invite the children to read out their list of alphabetical place names. Ask them to explain how they knew the order in which to write 'Birkdale' and 'Bonby'.

✦ Invite the children who completed Activity sheet 3 to explain how they matched the place names to their meanings. Ask them to explain how they knew the correct alphabetical order for 'Langtoft', 'Langthwaite' and 'Langwathby'.

---

 **Follow-up ideas for literacy**

✦ Discuss any new vocabulary the children have learned during the lesson, such as 'clearing', 'farmstead' and 'headland'. Ask them what similarities they notice between the Viking words and their meanings in English, for example 'dalr'/'dale', 'langr'/'long' and 'birki'/'birch'.

✦ Challenge the children to use dictionaries of place names to find the meanings of other place names of Viking origin, for example Boldron (Durham), Garstang (Lancashire) and Whitbeck (Cumbria).[2]

✦ Ask the children to use the index of a simple atlas or street map to look for given places or streets.

✦ Make a note of place names or street names on a simple map and compile an alphabetical index for the map.

---

 **Follow-up ideas for history**

✦ Give the children copies of maps of the United Kingdom, with the counties marked, and ask them to colour the counties in which they find places whose names come from the Vikings. Ask them to use word-processing software to create an alphabetical table on which they record place names of Viking origin, their meanings and the counties they are in.

✦ Ask the children to sort the data alphabetically by place name or county, using the table. Encourage them to look for trends in the data they collect, such as which counties have the most Viking place names?

✦ Show the children how to link their research into Viking place names with information from books about the places in which the Vikings were known (from other evidence) to have settled.

| Place name | Meaning | County |
|---|---|---|
| Birkenhead | headland with birch trees | Merseyside |
| Borrowdale | fort in a river valley | Cumbria |

---

**Place names from Old Norse and Old Scandinavian (the languages of the Vikings)**

**Birkenhead** (Merseyside) *birki* (birch) + *hofdi* = (headland) headland with birch trees.

**Borrowdale** (Cumbria) *borg* (fort) + *dalr* (river valley) = fort in a river valley.

**Braithwaite** (Cumbria) *breithr* (broad) + *thveit* (clearing) = broad clearing.

**Bratoft** (Lincolnshire) *breithr* (broad) + *toft* (homestead) = broad homestead.

**Copmanthorpe** (Yorkshire) *kaupmadr* (merchant) + *thorp* (village) = merchant's village.

**Crossens** (Merseyside) *krossar* (crosses) + *nes* (headland) = headland with crosses.

**Dalby** *dalr* (river valley) + *by*, from *bœr* (farm) = farm in a river valley.

**Derby** *dyrr* (deer) + *by*, from *bœr* (farm) = deer farm.

**Eakring** (Nottinghamshire) *eik* (oak) + *hringr* (ring) = ring of oaks.

**Grimsby** (Lincolnshire) *Grimur* (the name of a Norseman) + *by*, from *bœr* (farm) = Grimur's farm.

**Hardstoft** (Derbyshire) *Hjortr* (a Norseman's name) + *toft* (homestead) = Hjortr's homestead.

**Hesketh** (Lancashire) *hestr* (horse) + *skeithr* (race ground) = horse raceground

**Kirkby** (Merseyside, Lincolnshire, Yorkshire) *kirkja* (church) + *by*, from *bœr* (farm) = church farm.

**Lowestoft** (Suffolk) *Hlodver* (a Norseman's name) + *toft* (homestead) = Hlodver's homestead.

**Ravensworth** (North Yorkshire) *Hrafn* (a Norseman's name) + *vath* (ford) = Hrafn's ford.

**Solway** (Cumbria) *sula* (pillar) + *vath* (ford) = ford of the pillar.

**St Kilda** (off the west coast of Scotland) *skildir* (shields). When you look at them from a boat, the steep rocky islands have the shape of shields.

**York** *Jorvik*, Viking name for their settlement in the Anglo-Saxon village of Eoforwik (it had been named Eboracum by the Romans).

# ◆ Viking settlements ◆

✦ Read the glossary of Viking words and match the place names to their meanings.

✦ Write the place names next to their meanings in the chart. One has been done for you.

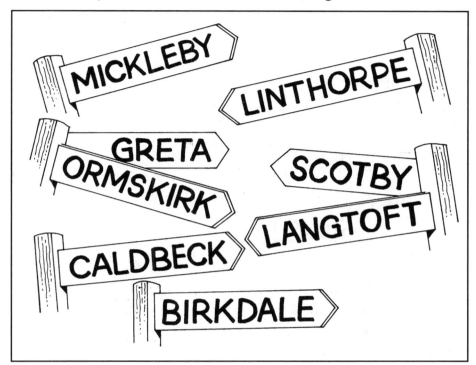

**Glossary**

**á** ('ow') river
**bekkr** stream
**birki** birch
**by** (bær) farm
**dalr** river valley
**grjot** stone
**kaldr** cold
**kirkja** church
**langr** long
**lin** flax
**mikill** large
**Ormr** a man's name
**thorp** village
**toft** homestead

| Place name | Meaning |
|---|---|
| Birkdale | Valley of birch trees |
| | Cold stream |
| | Stony river |
| | Long homestead |
| | Village where flax is grown |
| | Great farm |
| | Ormr's church |
| | Scot's farm |

## ✦Viking settlements✦

✦ Read the glossary of Viking words and match the place names to their meanings.

✦ Write the place names next to their meanings in the chart.

✦ On the back of this sheet, write the place names, with their meanings, in alphabetical order.

**Glossary**

**á** ('ow') river
**bekkr** stream
**birki** birch
**bondi** farmer
**by** (bær) farm
**dalr** river valley
**gas** geese
**gil** ravine
**grjot** stone
**kaldr** cold
**kirkja** church
**langr** long
**lin** flax
**mikill** large
**Ormr** a man's name
**thorp** village
**thveit** clearing
**toft** homestead
**vath** ford

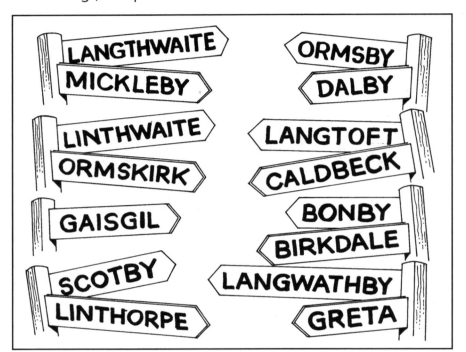

LANGTHWAITE　ORMSBY
MICKLEBY　DALBY
LINTHWAITE　LANGTOFT
ORMSKIRK　CALDBECK
GAISGIL　BONBY
　BIRKDALE
SCOTBY　LANGWATHBY
LINTHORPE　GRETA

| Place name | Meaning |
|---|---|
| | Clearing where flax is grown |
| | Scot's farm |
| | Great farm |
| | Ormr's church |
| | Farmer's farm |
| | Farm at a long ford |
| | Long clearing |
| | Stony river |
| | Village where flax is grown |
| | Long homestead |
| | Cold stream |
| | Ormr's farm |
| | Ravine where wild geese go |
| | Valley of birch trees |
| | Farm in a river valley |

# ◆ Viking settlements ◆

◆ Read the glossary of Viking words and match the place-names to their meanings.

◆ Write the place names on the chart in alphabetical order.

◆ Next to each place name write its meaning.

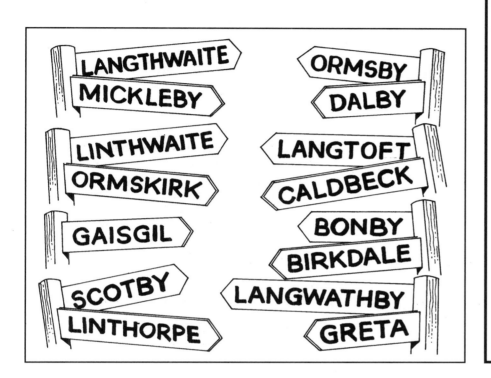

**Glossary**

**á** ('ow') river
**bekkr** stream
**birki** birch
**bondi** farmer
**by** (bær) farm
**dalr** river valley
**gas** geese
**gil** ravine
**grjot** stone
**kaldr** cold
**kirkja** church
**langr** long
**lin** flax
**mikill** large
**Ormr** a man's name
**thorp** village
**thveit** clearing
**toft** homestead
**vath** ford

| Place name | Meaning |
|---|---|
|  |  |
|  |  |
|  |  |
|  |  |
|  |  |
|  |  |
|  |  |
|  |  |
|  |  |
|  |  |
|  |  |
|  |  |
|  |  |
|  |  |
|  |  |

# Chapter 5

# Henry VIII

 **Literacy objectives**

✦ To read information passages and identify the main points by noting or underlining key words or phrases. (Y3, T1: T20)
✦ To learn how arguments are presented. (Y4, T3: T17)
✦ To use logical connectives in an argument. (Y4, T3: S4)

 **History objectives**

(Unit 7)
✦ To learn the names of Henry VIII's first two wives and the reasons for his marriages and his first divorce.
✦ To learn about the power and importance of a Tudor king.
✦ To understand some of the reasons for the break with the Roman Catholic Church.
✦ To understand key historical terms, such as 'treason', 'alliance' and 'succession'.

 **Resources**

✦ Pictures of Henry VIII and Catherine of Aragon.
✦ A Tudor family tree.
✦ A timeline which includes the sixteenth century.

**Starting point: Whole class**

✦ Tell the children that they are going to learn about the second Tudor king, Henry VIII. Ask the children to locate the year 1509, when Henry VIII came to the throne, on a timeline. Show them pictures of Henry VIII and ask them what they can find out about him from them.

✦ Discuss the reasons why people marry. Invite the children to talk about any recent marriages in their families. Explain that in royal families parents usually chose husbands and wives for their children in order to gain friendship or money from other countries. For example, Henry VII (Henry VIII's father) had tried to make peace with Scotland by marrying his daughter, Margaret, to James IV of Scotland.

✦ Ask the children between what ages people usually get married. Explain that in Tudor times people were engaged and even married when they were very young. Discuss the meanings of 'monarch', 'betrothed', 'alliance', 'treason' and 'succession'.

✦ Ask the children what they know about the Roman Catholic Church. Explain that it was the first Christian church and that other kinds of Christianity have developed from it. Ask them if they know the name of the present Pope and where he lives.
Explain the terms 'clergy', 'archbishop', 'Archbishop of Canterbury' and 'Lord Chancellor'.

 **Using the photocopiable text**

✦ Enlarge the text on page 30 or provide the children with copies. Explain that the information is taken from longer and more detailed written sources about Henry VIII. Read the text with the children and explain the meanings of words they do not know (or ask them to look them up). Ask them whether this is a fiction or non-fiction text. How can they tell?

✦ Tell the children that the purpose of the text is to explain why Henry VIII divorced Catherine of Aragon. Ask them to point out some of the key words and phrases.

✦ Talk about the differences between an argument and other texts: an argument gives different points of view and tries to convince people of the truth of one of those points of view. It gives evidence to support that point of view.

✦ Discuss the ways in which the children could use the information from the text to write an argument for or against Henry VIII's divorce. If they wanted to persuade people that the divorce was a good thing, which evidence would they choose? If they wanted to argue against it, which would they choose? Consider opposing points of view, for example 'The king should remarry so that he can have a son who will eventually become king,' and 'I think it's fine that he has a daughter who will become queen.'

✦ Model the use of logical connectives, for example 'They say that a woman will be a weak ruler. How do they know this? *Moreover*, do they not remember strong female rulers from the past, such as Cleopatra and Boudica?'

# Henry VIII

 **Group activities**

**Using the differentiated activity sheets**

**Activity sheet 1:** This is for children who can retell information from a non-fiction text. They can understand simple sentences and can say whether they support or oppose an action.

**Activity sheet 2:** This is for children who can recognise whether a statement supports or opposes an argument. They are learning to identify the key points in an argument.

**Activity sheet 3:** This is for children who can identify and mark the key points in a text. They can recognise those which support or oppose a proposition or action, and can use them in presenting an argument. They are developing their vocabulary of logical connectives.

**Plenary session**

✦ Invite the children who completed Activity sheet 1 to share their lists of arguments supporting and opposing Henry VIII's divorce. What do they think he should have done, and why?

✦ Move on to Activity sheet 2 and invite the children to explain why each statement supports or opposes Henry VIII's divorce. Challenge them to find any others in the passage on page 30.

✦ Make an enlarged copy of page 30 and invite the children who completed Activity sheet 3 to come out and underline the key words and phrases about Henry VIII's divorce. Ask them to read out their planned arguments.

 **Follow-up ideas for literacy**

✦ Provide other non-fiction passages and ask the children to find information about a particular topic and to mark the key words and phrases.

✦ Give the children passages which contain indirect speech and ask them to rewrite the spoken words in speech bubbles.

✦ Provide other arguments for the children to read and ask them to identify the useful connective words and phrases. Ask them to compile word banks of 'logical connectives'.

 **Follow-up ideas for history**

✦ Discuss Henry VIII's marriage to Anne Boleyn: did it solve his problem? Ask the children to read information books and make notes about what happened: the birth of Elizabeth and the execution of Anne Boleyn (and the reasons for it).

✦ Provide pictures of, and information about, Henry VIII's third, fourth, fifth and sixth wives and ask the children to find out why and how Henry ended each marriage (except the third and sixth).

✦ Provide information about Edward VI and ask the children if his birth solved Henry's problem. Show a copy of the portrait of Edward VI which is in the National Portrait Gallery. Explain that his clothes were padded to make him look much bigger and stronger. Ask the children why they think this is.

# Henry VIII's divorce

Catherine of Aragon

Henry VIII

Anne Boleyn

When Henry VIII became king, England was a Roman Catholic country. As now, the Pope was head of the Roman Catholic Church.

Royal marriages were often arranged to keep one country friendly with another. Henry VIII's father, Henry VII, had wanted an alliance with Spain. Henry VIII married Catherine of Aragon in 1509, the year he became king. She was the daughter of King Ferdinand and Queen Isabella of Spain and the niece of Charles V of France. She had been married to Henry's elder brother Arthur, who died.

Catherine and Henry had several babies, but they all died, except one – Mary. Henry was disappointed that none of his three sons survived. He wanted a son to take over as king when he died. At the time it was thought that a female ruler would be weak.

When Catherine was too old to have any more children, Henry fell in love with a younger woman – Anne Boleyn. He wanted to marry her, but the Roman Catholic Church allowed divorce only with special permission from the Pope.

The Pope would not give Henry permission to divorce Catherine of Aragon. Henry talked to his advisers about what to do. Thomas Cranmer, the Archbishop of Canterbury, said that Henry could declare his marriage to Catherine unlawful because she was his brother's widow. Sir Thomas More, the Lord Chancellor, said that he could not agree with divorce, because it was against the rules of the Church.

Henry declared himself head of the Church in England. He married Anne Boleyn in 1533. He demanded that all the clergy should swear an oath to accept him as head of the Church. Any who did not would be executed for treason. Henry would not allow anyone to oppose him. Most of the clergy took the oath, even if they privately disagreed with it, just to stay alive. Thomas More did not. He was found guilty of treason, and beheaded.

# ◆ An argument ◆

◆ Read what each person below is saying. Look for arguments for the divorce and against the divorce.

◆ Write the arguments on the chart.

Henry loves me, not Catherine.

England needs a king, not a queen.

The Church does not allow divorce.

The Pope

A nobleman

Anne Boleyn

Henry VIII's marriage to his brother's widow was unlawful.

I need a son who can rule England after I die.

Thomas Cranmer, the Archbishop of Canterbury

Henry VIII

I am the King's good servant, but God's first. I cannot agree to the divorce.

I am Henry's lawful wife. I shall always be his wife.

Sir Thomas More, the Lord Chancellor

Catherine of Aragon

| Arguments for the divorce | Arguments against the divorce |
|---|---|
| | |

◆ On the back of this sheet, write whether you think Henry should have been allowed to divorce or not, giving your reasons.

# ✦ An argument ✦

✦ Reread the text on page 30.
✦ Look for facts and opinions for and against Henry VIII's divorce.
✦ Underline the key points.
✦ Plan an argument for or against the divorce.

Include all the facts and opinions in your argument. Think of ways to argue against those which disagree with you.

| **Useful connectives** | | |
|---|---|---|
| and | finally | in the first place |
| after all | for example | on the other hand |
| also | however | so |
| but | in addition | therefore |

**Introduction** People were scared to disagree with Henry VIII about his divorce, but there are several reasons why he _____

_____

_____

**Paragraph 2** In the first place _____

_____

_____

_____

_____

**Paragraph 3** In addition _____

_____

_____

_____

_____

**Paragraph 4** Finally _____

_____

_____

_____

_____

**Conclusion** Therefore _____

_____

_____

_____

## ✦ An argument ✦

✦ Reread the text on page 30.
✦ Look for facts and opinions for and against Henry VIII's divorce.
✦ Underline the key points.
✦ Plan an argument for or against the divorce.

Include all the facts and opinions in your argument. Think of ways to argue against those which disagree with you.

| **Useful connectives** | | | |
|---|---|---|---|
| and | finally | in addition | so |
| after all | firstly | in the first place | therefore |
| also | for example | moreover | thus |
| but | however | on the other hand | whereas |

**Introduction** _____

_____

_____

**Paragraph 2** _____

_____

_____

_____

_____

**Paragraph 3** _____

_____

_____

_____

_____

**Paragraph 4** _____

_____

_____

_____

_____

**Conclusion** _____

_____

_____

_____

Chapter 6

# The rich and poor in Tudor times

 **Literacy objectives**

- To scan indexes, chapter and page headings and subheadings to locate information quickly and accurately. (Y3, T3: T17)
- To appraise a non-fiction book for its contents and usefulness by scanning it. (Y4, T2: T15)
- To scan texts to locate key words or phrases, useful headings and key sentences, and to use these as tools for summarising the text. (Y4, T2: T17)

 **History objectives**

(Unit 8)
- To distinguish between wealth and poverty in Tudor times.
- To learn about the lives of rich and poor people of Tudor times from evidence such as pictures.
- To select information to answer questions.

 **Resources**

- Pictures of Tudor houses.[3]
- Reproductions of paintings of scenes from Tudor times, showing people at different levels of society.[4]
- Colour pictures of Tudor clothing.[4]
- Information books on the Tudor period.

 **Starting point: Whole class**

- Tell the children that they are going to learn about how people lived in Tudor times and to compare the lives of rich and poor people. Can they tell whether people are rich or poor nowadays by looking at their clothes and possessions? What differences do they look for?

- Tell the children that in Tudor times a new fashion could take months to reach towns in the south of England from London, and up to fifteen years to reach country districts farther away. Why do they think this is? Ask them to compare that with today. Discuss the difference made by communication systems such as newspapers, television and the Internet. What differences are there between the fashions worn by rich and poor people? Discuss the different clothes people wear for their work.

- Ask the children about the other ways in which they can tell if people are rich or poor – their homes. Show pictures of homes from the Tudor period.

- Explain that during the reign of Henry VIII the population grew very quickly, there was not enough work for everyone, and there were often shortages of food. There was a rise in the number of beggars, who came to the towns where they hoped to find people who would help them. Do the children know how poor people are helped nowadays? Compare Tudor times with modern times.

 **Using the photocopiable text**

- Enlarge the text on page 36 or provide the children with copies. Explain that the pictures are based on drawings of real Tudor clothes and on paintings from the time. Tell them that there is a great deal more evidence about the clothes of rich people than those of poor people, because rich people paid artists to paint their portraits.

- Read the text with the children and explain the meanings of words they do not know, or encourage them to look them up.

- Ask the children to tell you how they could find more information about the differences between the lives of rich and poor people in Tudor times. Show them the collection of books on the Tudors. Ask them where they might look first to see if the books contain the information they need. Remind them about using the contents and index. Model the use of the index in some of the books to find information about Tudor clothes. What key words should we look for? How useful would these books be for our purpose? Go to some of the pages which were listed in the index for that topic; model how to scan the headings, subheadings and captions. Are these pages helpful? Which parts should we read in more detail to find the information we need?

 **Group activities**

**Using the differentiated activity sheets**

**Activity sheet 1:** This is for children who can scan headings and subheadings to find information. They can recognise when information answers a question.

**Activity sheet 2:** This is for children who can scan an index to find quickly the information they need to answer a question. They can make notes about which parts of a book will help them.

34

# The rich and poor in Tudor times

**Activity sheet 3:** This is for children who can make a note of key words for which they need to look when searching for information. They can quickly locate information by scanning a book and are learning to evaluate the usefulness of books they scan.

 *Plenary session*

✦ Ask the children who completed Activity sheet 1 which pages provide the information they need. Did they read subheadings and captions as well as main headings?

✦ Move on to Activity sheet 2 and invite the children to share some of their responses. How did they decide which pages would help them?

✦ Make an enlarged copy of Activity sheet 3, and complete it with some of the responses of children who worked on it.

---

 *Follow-up ideas for literacy*

✦ Give the children who completed Activity sheet 1 books about Tudor history clipped open at the pages they are to scan in order to decide quickly whether they give the information they want for a given question. How quickly can they decide? Ask them which are the best pages to use.

✦ Ask the children to make notes from the pages or books they have scanned in order to find information to answer a question about rich and poor people in Tudor times. Revise the use of abbreviations in note-taking, and other quick methods, such as omitting unnecessary words (for example, 'the' and 'a').

✦ In groups, let the children research and produce word-processed newspaper reports about the events leading to Henry VIII's divorce. Encourage them to think of headlines to engage the reader's interest (for instance 'KING TO BREAK WITH ROME' or 'MORE STANDS FIRM').

✦ Challenge higher-achieving children to write an appraisal of an information book[5], summarising the information it contained and commenting on how easy the book was to understand and how good the pictures were. They could also say how well the captions informed the reader about the pictures.

✦ In groups, ask the children to make and complete appraisal charts for the books they have read, for example:

| Title | Good index? | Good glossary? | Good pictures? | Good captions? | Easy to understand? |
|-------|-------------|----------------|----------------|----------------|---------------------|
|       |             |                |                |                |                     |

---

 *Follow-up ideas for history*

✦ Help the children to find out about the different classes of beggars in Tudor times and the laws passed about begging.

✦ Ask the children to find out how some rich people helped the poor (for example, by building almshouses, giving money to town councils to keep down the price of grain, etc.).

✦ Provide information about, and pictures of, life in the town and country and ask the children to compare the lives of people in both settings.

✦ If possible, visit a Tudor house and help the children to find the answers to questions such as 'How did they keep warm?', 'How did they cook?', 'How did they keep clean?' and 'What did they eat?'

### Nobles

Rich people could afford clothes made from silk, satin and velvet, and trimmed with lace, fur, feathers and jewels. They wore colourfully embroidered clothes, made from dyed materials and gold cloth, but only the nobility were allowed to wear blue velvet or deep red. It was fashionable to wear a stiff, starched ruff around the neck and gold and silver jewellery inlaid with precious stones. Their shoes were made from velvet or satin. Stockings were made of fine wool or cotton. Only the very rich wore silk stockings.

### Professional people

People like magistrates and members of other professions earned enough money to buy fashionable clothes, but not as fine as those of the nobility. They, too, would wear silks and velvets and have trimmings of embroidery, fur and feathers. They wore jewellery such as rings and brooches. Some of them might wear a ruff, but much smaller ruffs than those worn by nobles. They wore finely woven wool or cotton stockings.

### Manual workers

Farmers and other manual workers wore cheap, practical clothes. Their stockings were made of coarse wool or cotton. Shoes were made of leather and had thick soles. Men wore felt or woollen hats and canvas jerkins and women wore linen hoods and aprons over plain cotton gowns. Woollen and cotton clothes were made of homespun material in natural colours, or dyed blue or brown with vegetable dyes.

### Beggars

There were many beggars in Tudor times. Many of them could not find work; others were too old or unfit to work and had no one to support them. Others did not want to work. The only money, food or clothing they had were what other people gave them. This one has neither shoes nor stockings. He is wearing an old, ragged tunic, with no shirt under it.

# ◆ Planning research ◆

◆ Look at the the headings and captions on these pages from an information book about Tudor times.

◆ Which pages would help you to find out about the homes of rich and poor people? Complete the chart.

Some of the pages might not help you at all.

## Henry VIII and his six wives

ᴜᴍ ᴜᴇᴄ ᴜᴇᴄ ᴜᴇᴍ ᴀᴀ ᴜᴍ
ᴜᴍ ᴜᴇᴄ ᴜᴍ ᴍ ᴍ ᴜᴇᴄ

HENRY VIII

**Why did Henry divorce Catherine of Aragon?**

**1**

## Inside a Tudor farmhouse

WILLIAM OAK'S HOUSE

**How did they keep warm?**

**2**

## Hampton Court Palace

THE GREAT HALL

**Who lived at Hampton Court?**

**3**

## Bess of Hardwick

BESS OF HARDWICK

**Hardwick Hall, Bess's home...**

**4**

## Tudor kitchens

THE KITCHEN IN A PEASANT'S COTTAGE

**What did they eat?**

**5**

## Furniture

A CARVED CHAIR

**What kind of furniture did poor people have?**

**6**

| Useful pages about homes in Tudor times | |
|---|---|
| **Page** | **What it might tell me about the homes of rich and poor people** |
| | |
| | |
| | |
| | |
| | |

## ✦ Planning research ✦

✦ This page shows the index of an information book about Tudor times. Circle the words that might help you to find out about the homes of rich and poor people.

### Index

abbeys, 14
Aragon, Catherine of, 6, 12, 13
Armada, 40, 41

Bible, 14, 16, 35
Boleyn, Anne, 12, 13

castles, 21, 26, 27
church, 11–17
Cleves, Anne of, 13
country houses, 23, 26
court and courtiers, 19, 45
craftspeople and their homes, 45

Drake, Sir Francis, 38–40, 44

Edward VI, son of Henry VIII and Jane
    Seymour, 13
Elizabeth, Queen of England, daughter
    of Henry VIII and Anne Boleyn,
    12, 13

farms, 25, 26, 30
furniture, 31

gentry, 6, 45

glass, 30, 35
gold, 38–40
Grey, Lady Jane, 44, 45

Henry VIII, 7–15, 45
houses, 30, 33, 35
Howard, Catherine, 13

iron, 22, 35

London, 22, 23, 29, 40, 43

Mary, Queen of England, daughter of
    Henry VIII and Catherine of
    Aragon, 12
merchants, 5, 23, 25, 34, 37, 45

nobles, 5–7, 11, 14, 45

palaces, 6, 13
peasants, 14, 37, 45

servants, 14, 15, 45
Seymour, Jane, 13

town houses, 22, 23, 26, 27, 37, 40
tradespeople, 5, 25, 34, 37

yeomen, 5, 45

✦ What else could you look for to find out about the lives of rich and poor people?

_____

✦ Write the words from the index that would help you.

_____

_____

_____

✦ Which pages would you read?

_____

# ◆ Planning research ◆

What were the homes of the rich and the poor like in Tudor times?

◆ Choose a book that you think will give information about homes.
Plan how you will use it to answer this question.

◆ List the key words you will look for.

To help you to get started, some key words have been written for you.

| |
|---|
| materials: *brick, stone, glass, thatch, wood*<br>number of rooms:<br>decoration: |
| Title of book |

◆ Look through the book. Read the chapter and page headings and any subheadings.
Look at the pictures.

◆ Decide which parts of the book will help you.

| Useful parts of the book | What I shall find in each part |
|---|---|
| Useful chapters | |
| Useful pages | |
| Useful pictures | |

Chapter 7

# Children in World War II

 **Literacy objectives**

✦ To write letters linked to work in other subjects.
  (Y3, T3: T20)
✦ To organise letters into simple paragraphs. (Y3, T3: T23)
✦ To understand the differences between verbs in the first,
  second and third person relating to different types of
  text, for example recounts. (Y3, T2: S10)

 **History objectives**

(Unit 9)
✦ To learn about the areas which were targets for the blitz
  during World War II.
✦ To find out the reasons why children were evacuated.
✦ To find out from people's recollections about their
  experiences of evacuation.

 **Resources**

✦ A World War II map of the United Kingdom, showing the
  major cities.
✦ Pictures of evacuees.
✦ Newspaper or video reports about recent evacuations
  resulting from wars or natural disasters.

 **Starting point: Whole class**

✦ Before beginning this activity the children should
  already have learned about where and when World War
  II took place, the countries involved and why it started.
  They should also have learned about the ways in which
  the war was fought, including air raids.

✦ Have any of the children ever been away from home
  without their parents? Ask volunteers to describe their
  experiences. Discuss recent evacuations such as those
  caused by floods, wars and other disasters, and show the
  children pictures from newspapers (or recordings of
  television news reports). In what sorts of places did the
  evacuated people sleep or spend their days?

✦ Tell the children that they are going to learn about how
  people tried to keep their children safe during the war.
  Ask them why they think the government told people in
  cities to send their children to the country. Explain that
  people in the country who had enough room had to take
  in evacuees from cities and that there were billeting

officers whose job it was to inspect country people's
houses to check if they had enough room for evacuees.
Ask the children how people might have felt about
having to look after children they did not know. How do
they think the children felt?

✦ Show the children pictures of evacuees and discuss what
  can be seen in them: gas masks, name and address
  labels, luggage and so on.

 **Using the photocopiable text**

✦ Enlarge the text on page 42 or make a copy for each
  child. Explain that the text is based on the memories of
  a woman born in 1929, who was evacuated during
  World War II. Explain the meanings of terms such as
  'billeting officer', 'ration', 'blitz' and 'gas mask'.

✦ Ask the children how they can tell that this account is in
  the first person. They should identify verbs in the first
  person and point out the subject 'I' or 'we'. Encourage
  them to notice any verbs whose subject is not the first
  person and explain why.

✦ Ask the children what tense the account is written in,
  and why. They could give examples of verbs in the past
  tense and say what difference it would make if they were
  changed to the present.

✦ Tell the children that they are going to pretend to be
  evacuees and write a letter home. Ask them to tell you
  what things they might write about in this letter. Revise
  the format of a letter, pointing out where to write the
  sender's address and the date and how paragraphs are
  set out. Ask for examples of different endings for letters.
  Which ones would they use in a letter to someone in
  their family?

 **Group activities**

**Using the differentiated activity sheets**

**Activity sheet 1:** This is for children who have had
experience of writing simple messages and letters. They
know how to end an informal letter and are learning other
conventions of letter-writing. They need help in organising
a letter. They are learning about the purposes of letters and
how to recognise an account in the first person.

# Children in World War II

**Activity sheet 2:** This is for children who can write a simple, informal letter and are learning to organise their writing into paragraphs. They know how to set out a letter, but benefit from having a structure to help them in this. They know that a letter is written mainly in the first person and that, if it describes things which have happened, it is written in the past tense.

**Activity sheet 3:** This is for children who can write letters confidently. They can collect information written in different formats and rewrite it in the form of a letter. They can recognise first and third person accounts and are learning to change accounts from the third to the first person. They can organise a letter into paragraphs and are consolidating and developing this skill.

 *Plenary session*

✦ Invite the children who completed Activity sheet 1 to read out their letters. Ask the others to check them against the main points suggested in the speech bubbles. Invite them to comment on what they thought was good and make suggestions as to how the letters could be improved.

✦ Move on to Activity sheet 2. Display the six paragraph headings and invite one of the children to read the first paragraph of his or her letter. The others can say how well it describes the person's feelings. Invite another child to read out the second paragraph of his or her letter, while the others comment on how well it describes the people, and so on.

✦ Invite a child who completed Activity sheet 3 to read his or her letter. Ask the others to check that the verbs are in the correct tense and person.

 *Follow-up ideas for literacy*

✦ Provide an opportunity for the children to interview people from the local community who were evacuated during World War II. Encourage them to prepare for their interviews by making notes on what they already know about evacuation and what they would like to find out. Ask them to prepare questions to ask their interviewees.

✦ Some children could use tape recorders (with the permission of the interviewees) to record the interviews. Others could take notes. Remind them of the ways in which they can take notes quickly and accurately – for example, by using abbreviations and omitting non-essential words (see Chapter 1).

✦ In groups, challenge the children to plan and write plays based on what they have learned about evacuation. Show them (or revise) how to set out the text for a play, which they could enact in their groups. Encourage them to edit and redraft their writing.

 *Follow-up ideas for history*

✦ Give the children selected sources (such as photographs, extracts from novels, letters and memoirs) to find out about evacuation. Ask them to compare the experiences of different evacuees.

✦ Help the children to find out what life was like in British cities during World War II, the safety precautions people took and why they were encouraged to send their children to the country.

They could look at copies of wartime newspapers, and news extracts, both printed and electronic.

✦ Look at pictures of air-raid shelters and read newspaper advertisements for them. Read blackout instructions for homes and vehicles, and find out about the work of air-raid wardens. Ask the children to write an account of life in a city during the blitz.

# The Blitz

The Second World War put an end to a lovely day out on the beach at Mablethorpe. It was 3 September 1939. My father had borrowed Speedy Webster's Model T Ford to take the family on holiday. My sister and I carried on building a sandcastle and my father read his newspaper. But my mother leapt to her feet and started packing our things, stopping only to give fearful looks out to sea. Any minute, she thought, a bomber would appear over the horizon.

On the drive home we passed truckloads of soldiers in their khaki uniforms. They waved and smiled. It did not occur to us that they might soon be killed in the war.

The next day, at school in Liverpool, we heard about evacuation. That meant we would be sent to live with a family in the country until the war was over. I was ten and my sister was twelve.

My mother spent two days washing and ironing our clothes and packing them into pillowcases (few families could spare a suitcase). I had a name and address label pinned on to my coat. There was great excitement as we arrived at school with our gas masks in cardboard boxes and, of course, our pillowcases. I wondered why so many adults were crying as their children were setting off on this great adventure.

We arrived at the local station to see crowds of children from other schools and we all piled on to the train to North Wales. From the station in Mold the billeting officer took us to the Assembly Rooms. 'I only want boys', 'I can take one,' we heard as people looked along the line of children and picked out the ones they liked the look of.

'Auntie Meg' and 'Uncle John' took us back to 'The Firs', in Holm Lane. They treated us as if we were their own children. We heard that other children never got their letters from home, or the chocolate from the weekly ration parcels sent to evacuees.

One morning Auntie Meg and Uncle John took us up Moel Famau to watch the dawn breaking, but we saw something much more exciting – the morning air raid over Liverpool. It didn't frighten us at all; it was just like fireworks. It was only when we returned home that we realised how much damage the bombs had done.

# ✦ A letter ✦

✦ Imagine you are the evacuee in the text.
✦ Write a letter from her to her parents.

## Useful words

| | | | |
|---|---|---|---|
| bombs | friends | mountains | today |
| countryside | happy | parcel | tomorrow |
| enjoying | kind | quiet | unkind |
| family | letter | school | well |
| fields | mean | this week | yesterday |

The Firs,

Holm _____

_____

_____

_____

Fill in the address where you are staying.

Date _____ 1939

Dear _____

I have arrived safely in _____

I am staying with _____

_____

_____

_____

Tell your parents about the people you are staying with.

Some of the other evacuees want to go home. _____

_____

_____

_____

Tell them about other evacuees who are not so lucky.

_____

_____

Write about what you have done and seen.

_____

Say how you feel.

_____

_____

End the letter.

## ✦ A letter ✦

✦ Write a letter from the evacuee in the text to her parents.

✦ Plan the letter in paragraphs:

    1. How you are feeling.

    2. The people you are staying with.

    3. Your new school and new friends.

    4. The experiences of other evacuees you have met.

    5. What it is like in the country and what you have done and seen.

    6. Asking how your parents are.

Look for clues in the text.

Address _____

_____

_____

_____

Date _____

Dear _____

How will you end the letter?

# ✦ A letter ✦

✦ Reread the text, and read other information about evacuees.

✦ Write a letter from a Second World War evacuee to his or her parents.
Tell them about the journey, where he or she was taken and how the evacuee
was chosen by a family. Describe the evacuee's experiences in this family's home.
Say how it is different from his or her own home in the city.

Look for clues in the text.

How will you end the letter?

# Wartime fare

 ## Literacy objectives

✦ To learn how written instructions are organised and to recognise the importance of the correct sequence. (Y3, T2: T14)
✦ To write instructions. (Y3, T2: T16)
✦ To change verbs from the past to the present tense. (Y4, T1: S2)

 ## History objectives

(Unit 9)
✦ To learn about the diet of people during World War II.
✦ To learn why rationing was necessary and how it was organised.
✦ To learn about the impact of rationing on the lives of people in Britain during World War II.

 ## Resources

✦ A ration book (or a replica).
✦ Wartime recipes.

 ## Starting point: Whole class

✦ Before beginning this activity the children should already have learned about where and when World War II took place, the countries involved and why it started.

✦ Tell the children that they are going to learn about the foods people ate during World War II and how the war affected what could be bought.

✦ Show the children a ration book and explain what it was for. Tell them that there were shortages of many foods because ships bringing food from other countries were bombed by enemy planes, or torpedoed by submarines. Explain that rationing was a method of giving everyone a fair share of the food which was available.

✦ Show the children wartime and modern recipe books and ask them to notice any similarities and differences between everyday meals and between celebration meals. Which foods are absent from wartime recipes? Ask them to explain these absences: imports were severely hampered; also, certain foods people eat today had not become popular in Britain at that time.

 ## Using the photocopiable text

✦ Enlarge the text on page 48 or make a copy for each child. Explain that the text contains recipes for typical wartime food. Ask the children how they can recognise that they are recipes by scanning the layout and headings. Discuss the features of the layout of recipes: the picture which shows the dish, the heading and subheadings to help readers to plan their cooking, the list of ingredients at the beginning and the step-by-step instructions, in the correct order.

✦ Read the text with the children and explain any words or abbreviations they do not understand, particularly the measures and culinary terms such as 'strain', 'grated' and 'dried egg'.

✦ Point out the form of the verb in which the recipes are written (the imperative). Invite the children to give examples they hear in school of verbs in the imperative form. Ask them what this form of verb is used for.

✦ Look at how the verbs are used in the recipe. For example, in the line 'Peel or scrub potatoes, cut into small pieces and boil until soft' the verbs are imperative verbs, ones giving an instruction. These are neither in the past nor the present tense. How would we express this if we put it into the past tense? ('I peeled the potatoes, cut them into small pieces and boiled them until soft.') The sentence is no longer an instruction but a statement (it gives information in the form of a recount).

✦ Discuss the language of recipes: it is formal; it is addressed to a large audience not known to the writer; it does not use the words 'you' or 'I'.

✦ Rewrite one of the sentences in a much longer form – for example, 'Drain off the water in the pan in which you boiled the potatoes until there is none left, leave the potatoes in the pan and then mash them.' Ask them how they can make the sentence as short as possible without losing any important information. Point out that words such as 'the' can be omitted.

# Wartime fare

 ## Group activities

### Using the differentiated activity sheets

**Activity sheet 1:** This is for children who can recognise a recipe and know that it gives instructions. They know that a recipe has a heading to say what it is for and they are learning about the ways in which the layout of a recipe helps the reader. They are learning that it is important to give instructions in the correct order.

**Activity sheet 2:** This is for children who know that a recipe gives instructions in the correct order and about the ways in which its layout helps the reader. They are learning how to write sentences in the shortest possible way, omitting unnecessary words and using abbreviations.

**Activity sheet 3:** This is for children who understand the layout of recipes and the importance of writing instructions in the correct order. They know that recipes need to use brief, concise language and are learning how to change verbs from the past to the imperative and to write them in the correct form for instructions.

 ## Plenary session

✦ Invite the children who completed Activity sheet 1 to read out their recipes. Ask the others to check that nothing has been omitted and that the order of the instructions makes sense. Also ask them to comment on where the children have placed the headings and picture.

✦ Display the text of Activity sheet 2 and read it out. Ask the children what is wrong with it and invite those who completed the activity sheet to demonstrate how they changed it.

✦ Display the text from Activity sheet 3 and ask the class if it is a recipe. Ask them how it needs to be changed and invite those who completed the activity to demonstrate how they did this. Discuss the difference between the past tense and the imperative tense.

---

 ## Follow-up ideas for literacy

✦ Provide the opportunity for the children to make some of the dishes for which recipes are given in the text and the activity sheets. Ask them to make charts on which to evaluate the recipes.[6]

✦ Ask the children to rewrite a recipe as a picture sequence with captions, perhaps for younger children to read.

✦ Collect and display different types of instructions and ask the children to identify their purposes – for example, those for road safety, washing clothes, using equipment, assembling furniture and filling in order forms.

✦ Ask the children to convert into instructions any recounts or explanations they have written (for example, about how they solved a problem, found information or constructed something). This could be linked with science and technology.

---

 ## Follow-up ideas for history

✦ Play recordings of wartime radio broadcasts about food, for example 'The Radio Doctor' with his advice on vitamins and other nutrients in foods, and other Ministry of Food advice. Display copies of wartime posters encouraging people to eat foods grown in Britain, and pictures of cartoon characters such as 'Potato Pete'. Ask the children what they can find out from these sources about the foods which were grown in Britain and the foods which were in short supply.

✦ Arrange for the children to interview older people about the foods they ate during World War II and about shortages. They could find out how people avoided wasting food, and about their recipes for using up leftovers.

✦ Challenge the children to plan a week's wartime menu for a family. They could use ration books, instructions issued by the Ministry of Food for using rations and 'points', and wartime recipe books.

# Wartime recipes

## Potato cheese

Serves 4
Cooking time: 25 minutes

### Ingredients
2lb potatoes (old or new)
6–8oz grated cheese
2oz oatmeal
salt and pepper
2 tbsp chopped parsley

### Method
Peel or scrub potatoes, cut into small pieces and boil until soft.
Strain and mash in the pan.
Mix in half the grated cheese and the parsley.
Add salt and pepper to taste.
Turn mixture into a shallow dish.
Sprinkle on the rest of the cheese and the oatmeal.
Brown under grill.
Serve with cabbage or spinach.

## Raisin crisps

Quantity: 24 biscuits
Cooking time: 20 minutes

### Ingredients
3oz SR flour (or plain flour with 1 tsp baking powder)
1oz margarine
1oz sugar
1oz raisins
1 tbsp dried egg
1/2 cup milk to mix

### Method
Pre-heat oven to 350°F (Gas mark 4).
Mix together sugar, flour and dried egg.
Rub in margarine.
Add raisins.
Mix in enough milk to make firm dough.
Roll out thinly and cut into rounds (about 2" across).
Bake for 20 mins.

# ✦ A recipe ✦

This recipe has been mixed up.

✦ Cut it out and put it in the correct order.

✦ Reread the recipe and check that it makes sense.

| | |
|---|---|
| Serve with a raw vegetable salad. | **Potato Jane** |
| When dish is full pour on milk and bake for 45–60 minutes. | **Ingredients** |
| Add a layer of chopped leek, a layer of grated cheese and a layer of breadcrumbs. | $1\frac{1}{4}$ lb sliced potatoes<br>1 leek, chopped<br>2oz breadcrumbs |
| Put a layer of sliced potatoes in the bottom of an ovenproof dish. | 3oz grated cheese<br>salt and pepper<br>$\frac{1}{2}$ pt milk |
| Sprinkle salt and pepper on to each layer. | |
| Keep on adding layers until dish is full. | |
| Cooking time: 45– 60 minutes | |
| Finish with a layer of cheese and crumbs. | |
| Pre-heat oven to 350°F  (gas mark 4). | |
| **Method** | |
| Serves 4 people | |

# A recipe

✦ Write this recipe in the shortest way you can.
✦ Reread it to check that it still makes sense.

(Use abbreviations.)

(Think about layout and headings.)

(Take out words that are not needed.)

This is how to make Potato Jane. It will take between forty-five and sixty minutes to cook. There will be enough for four people. You will need the following ingredients: one and a quarter pounds of potatoes, a leek, two ounces of breadcrumbs, three ounces of cheese, salt and pepper and half a pint of milk.

This is what to do: First of all turn on the oven. If it is an electric oven, set it at three hundred and fifty degrees Fahrenheit; if it is a gas oven, set it on mark four. Cut the potatoes into slices and chop the leek. Use a cheese grater to grate the cheese. In the bottom of an ovenproof dish, spread a layer of sliced potato to cover the bottom of the dish. On top of the layer of sliced potato, spread a layer of leek and then sprinkle on some salt and pepper. On top of that spread a layer of cheese and sprinkle on some salt and pepper. One top of that spread a layer of breadcrumbs and sprinkle on some salt and pepper. Continue adding layers on top of one another until you have filled the dish to the top and then pour over the milk. Put the dish in the oven and bake the Potato Jane for between forty-five minutes and sixty minutes.

_____
_____
_____
_____
_____
_____
_____
_____
_____
_____
_____
_____

# ✦ A recipe ✦

✦ Read this recount about making a wartime dish called Potato Jane.

✦ Rewrite it as a recipe.

✦ Change the form of each verb.

✦ Write the sentences in the shortest possible way.

I made enough Potato Jane for four people. To do this I used one and a quarter pounds of potatoes, a leek, two ounces of breadcrumbs, three ounces of cheese, salt and pepper and half a pint of milk.

First I turned on the oven and pre-heated it to three hundred and fifty degrees Fahrenheit (that is the same as gas mark four). Then I sliced one and a half pounds of potatoes and chopped half a leek. Then I grated three ounces of cheese. After that I placed a layer of sliced potato in the bottom of the dish and continued filling the dish with layers of leek, cheese and breadcrumbs, finishing with a layer of cheese and breadcrumbs.
I sprinkled salt and pepper on to each layer. The last thing I added to the dish was the milk.
I poured half a pint of milk over the top before baking the Potato Jane for forty-five to sixty minutes. I served it with a very nice raw vegetable salad.

_____
_____
_____
_____
_____
_____
_____
_____
_____
_____
_____
_____
_____
_____
_____
_____
_____

# Ancient Egypt

 **Literacy objectives**

✦ To identify typical themes of mythology. (Y3, T2: T2)
✦ To be able to write a story plan for own myth, using a theme from reading but substituting different characters or changing the setting. (Y3, T2: T9)

 **History objectives**

(Unit 10)
✦ To recognise that the past can be split into periods such as ancient and modern.
✦ To answer questions about the past by making observations about sources of information.
✦ To learn about the religion of Ancient Egypt from sources such as myths.

 **Resources**

✦ Pictures of Ancient Egyptian deities including Re, Isis, Osiris, Horus, Seth and Thoth.
✦ Pictures of hieroglyphics.

 **Starting point: Whole class**

✦ Before beginning this activity the children should already have learned about the location of Egypt and placed the period known as 'Ancient Egypt' on a timeline. They should also have located the River Nile on a map of Egypt.

✦ Show the children pictures and hieroglyphics and explain that archaeologists and historians were able to find out a great deal from them about Ancient Egyptian religion.

✦ Point out in the pictures the gods and goddess Re, Isis, Osiris, Horus, Seth and Thoth, and tell the children that they are going to learn about the myths connected with these gods and goddess and about the beliefs of the Ancient Egyptians.

 **Using the photocopiable text**

✦ Enlarge the text on page 54 or make a copy for each child. Explain that it is a simplified version of other, more detailed and complicated texts.

✦ Read the text. Explain any words the children do not understand, or encourage them to look the words up.

✦ Tell the children that the text is a myth and explain the meaning of 'myth'. Ask them about other myths they have read, and discuss their similarities. Point out that in many cultures myths explained things which people did not understand, such as the creation of the world.

✦ Discuss the themes of traditional stories, legends and other myths the children have read. Ask them to identify any themes in this myth. Point out the power struggle, jealousy, trials of strength and struggles between good and evil.

✦ Discuss other myths in which the main characters have magic powers and how they use these powers. Show the children how to make a chart on which to record the types of character and the themes of myths (including Ancient Greek myths).

| Myth | Country of origin | Characters | Themes |
|------|-------------------|------------|--------|
| Isis and Osiris | Egypt | Re, Isis, Osiris, Horus, Seth, Thoth | Good and evil, power struggle, jealousy, trials of strength |

 **Group activities**

**Using the differentiated activity sheets**

**Activity sheet 1:** This is for children who can fill in the gaps in a summary of the main points of a story. They are to use this completed summary to help them to plan their own myth, which could be about Isis and Osiris or about another god or gods.

**Activity sheet 2:** This is for children who can make notes about the main points of the story of Isis and Osiris. They are provided with a structure to help them to write them in the correct order. This will then be the basis for them to write their own myth.

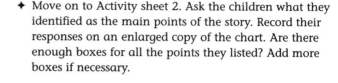

# Ancient Egypt

**Activity sheet 3:** This is for children who can identify the theme and main points of a myth and are learning to use myths they read as structures for writing their own. The activity sheet provides the children with a structure to help them to write their own myth about Ancient Egyptian gods and goddesses, inventing their own characters and planning the sequence of the story.

 *Plenary session*

✦ Display an enlarged copy of Activity sheet 1. Invite the children who completed it to say how they filled in the gaps. Would they have added anything else had there been space?

✦ Move on to Activity sheet 2. Ask the children what they identified as the main points of the story. Record their responses on an enlarged copy of the chart. Are there enough boxes for all the points they listed? Add more boxes if necessary.

✦ Invite the children who completed Activity sheet 3 to read out their story plans, while the others listen and suggest ways in which the stories could be improved.

 *Follow up-ideas for literacy*

✦ Ask the children to introduce speech into the original myth. Invite them to consider what the characters might have said in each scene and how they might have said it. They could create a wall display in the form of an Egyptian-style frieze, using paintings they have made of the characters and adding speech bubbles to tell the story.

✦ Revise quotation marks. Give each child a scene of the story to rewrite. They should write the text and use quotation marks to indicate speech.

✦ Convert the original myth into a play, with the speech added by the children. Explain the conventions of drama and ask each group to plan one or two scenes.

 *Follow-up ideas for history*

✦ Provide information books about Ancient Egypt and ask the children to record the information they collect on a chart.

| Homes | Education | Daily life | Death |
|-------|-----------|------------|-------|
|       |           |            |       |

✦ Show the children a picture or replica of an object from Ancient Egypt, such as a mummy, funeral mask, figurine, pot or jewellery. Ask them to draw and describe the object. Help them to relate the object to what they have learned about Ancient Egypt – for example, why might bodies have been embalmed and mummified? Encourage them to relate this question to what they have learned about life after death.

# Isis and Osiris

The chief Egyptian god was Re, god of the Sun and of creation. His daughter, Isis, had magical powers; she could turn herself into any creature and travel through earth, air, fire and water with ease. Isis was married to Osiris. Everyone respected Osiris as a good ruler of Egypt, who had spread civilisation far and wide. His brother Seth, god of darkness and chaos, was jealous of him, and planned to murder Osiris, so that he could rule Egypt instead.

Seth had Osiris measured in secret and had a beautiful coffer made, just the right size to fit him. Then Seth held a splendid banquet. He showed the guests the wonderful coffer and said that anyone who fitted into it exactly could keep it. One after another the guests tried to get into the coffer. Some could not squeeze in; their legs or arms or head stuck out. Others had space to spare. Then Seth asked Osiris to try; he fitted in exactly, of course.

No sooner was Osiris inside the coffer than Seth slammed the lid. He had the coffer thrown into the River Nile. It came to rest in a swamp, by a tamarisk tree. The tree grew all around the coffer, hiding it.

In tears, Isis went in search of the coffer. But Seth found it first, and cut the body of Osiris into fourteen pieces and scattered the pieces around the swamp. Isis did not give up. She collected the pieces and put them together. She asked Thoth, the Moon-god, for help. Thoth knew the magic spells to help the dead to pass through the underworld, the kingdom of the dead. He made Osiris ruler of the underworld.

Isis and Osiris had a son, Horus. When he grew up he challenged Seth for the throne of Egypt. They fought many times; sometimes they turned themselves into wild beasts. When they became huge black bulls and gored one another, Isis used her magic powers to kill them.

The gods held a meeting, but could not decide who had won. Then Osiris spoke from the underworld. He had created barley, he said, and neither gods nor people could survive without it, and so his son, Horus, should be declared the winner. The gods did not agree, so Osiris threatened to send savage messengers to drag them all to the underworld. That did the trick.

That was how Osiris became the god of resurrection, and the Ancient Egyptians came to believe in life after death.

# ✦ Planning a myth ✦

✦ Plan your own myth about the gods and goddesses of Ancient Egypt. You could base your myth on the story of Isis and Osiris, and change some of the events and characters.

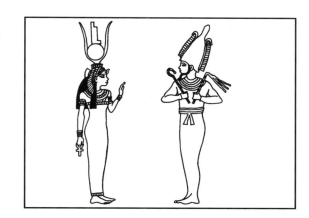

| | **Isis and Osiris myth** | **Your myth** |
|---|---|---|
| Title | | |
| Characters | Isis and her husband Osiris, Horus (their son), Seth (brother of Osiris), Thoth (the Moon-god) | |
| The problem | Seth was jealous of _____ | |
| What happened because of the problem | Seth tricked Osiris into getting into a coffer, locked him in and threw the coffer into the R_____ N_____ Horus and _____ turned themselves into _____ and fought. Isis _____ The gods could not decide _____ | |
| How the problem was solved | Osiris said he would send all the gods to the _____ Osiris became god of resurrection, and the Ancient Egyptians came to believe in _____ | |

# ◆ Planning a myth ◆

◆ Plan your own myth about the gods and goddesses of Ancient Egypt. You could base your myth on the story of Isis and Osiris, and change some of the events and characters.

|  | **Isis and Osiris myth** | **Your myth** |
|---|---|---|
| Title |  |  |
| Characters |  |  |
| The problem |  |  |
| What happened because of the problem |  |  |
| How the problem was solved |  |  |

# ✦ Planning a myth ✦

✦ Plan your own myth about the gods and goddesses of Ancient Egypt. You could base your myth on the story of Isis and Osiris, and change some of the events and characters.

| **Title** | |
|---|---|
| **Characters** | Say what is special about the characters and who is related to whom. |
| **Introduction** | What is the problem which causes the events of the story to happen? |
| **Main events** | What happens? |
| **Resolution** | How is the problem solved? |

# A local study

## Literacy objectives

+ To use a chart to make a record of information collected. (Y3, T1: T21)
+ To collect information from a variety of sources. (Y4, T2: T23)

## History objectives

(Unit 18)

+ To use maps to assist with a description of characteristic features of an area in the past.
+ To learn about the different sources of information about an area in the past.
+ To make deductions from physical evidence.
+ To recognise that some questions can be answered by looking at buildings, but others cannot.

## Resources

+ Old maps of a section of the local area.
+ Pictures of the same area in the past.
+ For Activity sheet 3, photographs of another area in the present day.

## Starting point: Whole class

+ Before beginning this activity the children should have made preliminary observations about the local area, noting interesting features which could be linked with the past – for example, any structures, remains and name plates.

+ Discuss the children's observations and help them to formulate questions which can be answered by looking at maps and old photographs of the area.

+ Show them an old map and old pictures of the area they have looked at and invite them to read out their questions. Help them to find old pictures and maps and to look for the features they have observed. Note some of the features which were present in the past and those which are related to other features from the past (such as the names of streets and buildings and the remains of buildings and other structures).

+ Tell the children that they are going to learn how others have found out about their local area's past from maps and old pictures.

## Using the photocopiable text

+ Enlarge the text on page 60, and cover all but the first section, headed 'Observations on Cornsay'.

+ Explain that the text begins with observations (in note form) made about a small rural village. It then lists questions which arose from the observations and goes on to say what was discovered from old maps and pictures.

+ Read the first part of the text with the children and ask them what questions they would ask if this were their local area. Record their responses and ask them how they could find the answers to their questions.

+ Uncover the questions on page 60 and compare them with the children's questions. Ask them to predict the answers to the questions. Discuss what can sometimes be deduced from observations, and then reveal the information in the text which was found from old maps, photographs and people's memories.

## Group activities

**Using the differentiated activity sheets**

**Activity sheet 1:** This is for children who know that captions give information about pictures. They can infer the meanings of words they do not understand by considering their context. They can write questions and are learning to focus their questions to help them to find out more about a topic.

**Activity sheet 2:** This is for children who know that notes are a shortened way of writing things and that they should be accurate. With support, they can write the type of question which will help them to find out about a topic.

**Activity sheet 3:** This is for children who can make notes quickly and accurately and formulate questions based on their notes. They are learning to use the questions they write to direct their research on a topic.

# A local study

## Plenary session

✦ Display an enlarged copy of Activity sheet 1. Invite the children who completed it to read out their questions. Help them to refine their questions – for example, by suggesting an alternative to 'What is this?' ('Was there something else joined on to the steps?')[7]

✦ Move on to Activity sheet 2. Ask the children to read out some of their questions, and encourage them to express the deductions they have made, for example 'Was there a mill on the site of the modern house named "The King's Mill"?', 'Was "Cuffs Bar" once a police station?', 'Did the flour and provender dealer deal in flour from a local mill?' Ask them to explain their questions.[7]

✦ Invite the children who completed Activity sheet 3 to share their answers with the class. Use this to help the class to decide on the kind of information they could include in observations of their own locality, and the kinds of questions they could ask in order to find out about its past.

## Follow-up ideas for literacy

✦ Ask the children to make notes on their observations of their local area and use them as the basis for a non-chronological report. Encourage them to write the deductions they make from their observations.

✦ Help the children to make use of the information they gather during their historical research to write a story set in their locality in the past.

✦ Develop the use of adjectives in writing descriptions. Encourage the children to use a thesaurus to broaden the range of adjectives in their vocabulary.

## Follow-up ideas for history

✦ Give the children two maps of the same area, one modern and one old. Ask them to list the differences they notice – for example, buildings and roads which have appeared or disappeared.

✦ Use census information and trade directories to find out about the changes in the numbers of people living in the locality and their occupations.

✦ Make a timeline with copies of drawings and paintings and old and recent photographs to show how your locality has changed over time.

## Observations on Cornsay

Smithy Cottage

The post box

Three roads in village. None named. Row of old cottages: Post Office Cottages, but no post office. Houses look old because built from the same kind of weathered old stone, slate roofs. On village green old cottage – Smithy Cottage. On one side big doorway, with door like garage door, but much bigger than most garages. Not far from it, post box set into quite modern octagonal structure made from bricks and breeze blocks covered with concrete. On side of it facing road, at ground level, a small lintel of old stone supported by two other pieces of old stone. Opposite post box: new house – Draw Well House. No draw-well. Next to Draw Well House, remains of old stone building. Walls crumbling and roof has fallen in. Broken slates inside the building. In front of it: walled garden (dry-stone walls). Ground beside garden very bumpy.

## Questions

- How did Post Office Cottages get their name? Was there a post office? Why would a village of only about fifteen houses need a post office?
- Why is it called Smithy Cottage? Was it a blacksmith's forge?
- Was the odd-looking structure on the village green built to hold the post box? If so, why is it so big?
- How did Draw Well House get its name? Was there a well there?
- What was the derelict building beside Draw Well House? Could it have been a farm building?

## Evidence from the Internet, old maps and pictures, and older people

All houses on 1861 map (shows 'Smithy'). People remember blacksmith. Census said population in 1891 = 2327. Older people remember village much bigger. Pointed to bumps in ground by Draw Well House (remains of cottages). Old picture of post office at Post Office Cottages. Old picture of derelict building (small Co-op store). People remember draw-well (now filled in and built over – octagonal structure on village green). Old stone lintel was over entrance.

**Activity 1**

# Notes and questions

✦ Look at the pictures and read the captions.
✦ What would you like to find out about the old things?
✦ Write eight questions.

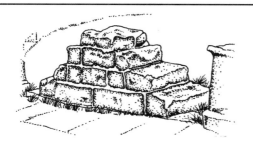

Steps made of sandstone, 60cm high.
Outside church hall of Holy Trinity Church.

Horseshoe prints about 150cm up on a
sandstone wall in Childwall Road.

An old sandstone building near the end of
Lake Road.

A stone set in the grass just inside the railings
of children's playground at end of Mill Lane.

## Questions

1 _____

2 _____

3 _____

4 _____

5 _____

6 _____

7 _____

8 _____

©Hopscotch Educational Publishing

# ◆ Notes and questions ◆

◆ Read the notes below about part of Liverpool.
◆ Write some questions which could be answered using old maps and
   pictures and by talking to older people.

---

**Old buildings**

Triangle of grass with a small, old, two-storey building (octagonal), worn sandstone.
97 High St (sandstone terrace) has date 1766.

---

**Other old structures**

Old sandstone steps. Leading to flat platform.
Very worn. Lichen and moss.
Four steps on each side, on edge of grass verge
outside church hall of Church of Holy Trinity.
Old sandstone cross in Monkswell Drive carved with
circles and flowers.

---

**Remains**

Old millstone and four big blocks of stone in garden of house named 'The King's Mill'
(modern house on hill with ground sloping away on all sides). No mill.

---

**Names and signs**

Bar named 'Cuffs'. Old sandstone building. Old lantern with blue glass over doorway. High
above doorway coat of arms carved in stone: '1879'. Nearby, restaurant & bar named
'Wavertree Town Hall'. Same crest above. Flaking paint on wall of TV repair shop: 'Flour and
provender dealer'. Monkswell Drive. Mill Lane. Mill Cottages. Lake Road. No mill. No lake.

---

**Questions**

_____
_____
_____
_____
_____
_____
_____
_____
_____
_____

**Name** _____

## ◆ Notes and questions ◆

✦ Complete the chart with your observations about photographs of a village, part of a town or a suburb in the present day.

✦ In note form, describe what you notice.

✦ Write questions to which you can find the answers.

**Old buildings**

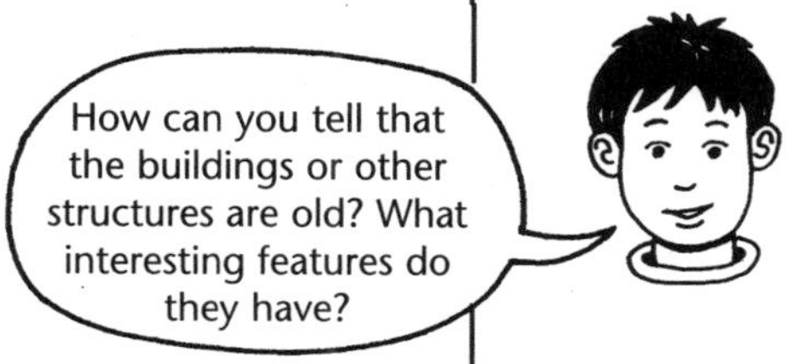

How can you tell that the buildings or other structures are old? What interesting features do they have?

**Other old structures**

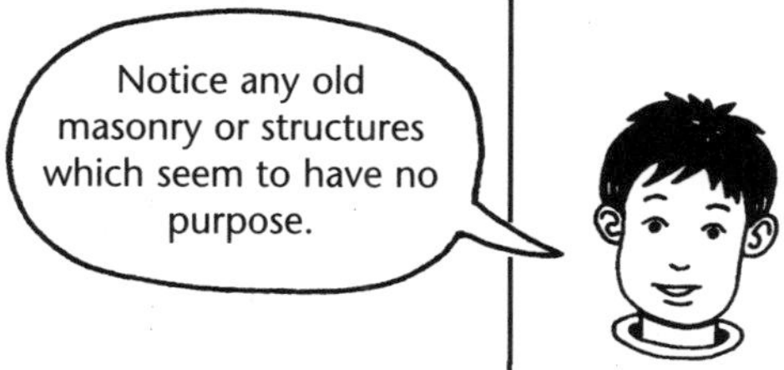

Notice any old masonry or structures which seem to have no purpose.

**Remains**

**Names and signs**

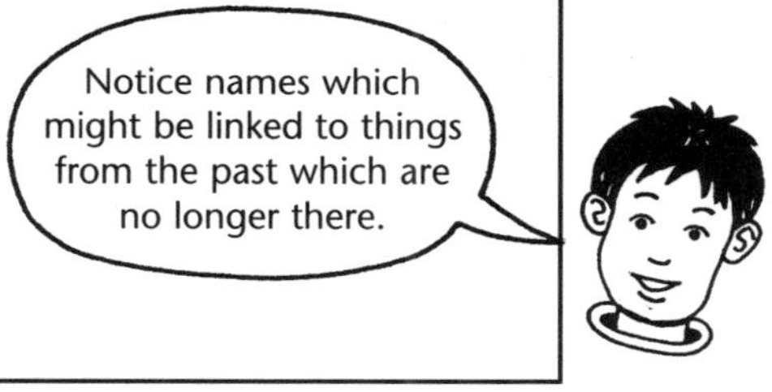

Notice names which might be linked to things from the past which are no longer there.

**Questions**

_____
_____
_____
_____
_____
_____
_____
_____
_____

©Hopscotch Educational Publishing

1 There has been much speculation about the identity of the person commemorated by the ship burial at Sutton Hoo, and why there was no skeleton found there. One suggestion is that it was Æthelhere, an Anglo-Saxon king killed in AD665 at the battle of Winwald in Northumbria and whose body was swept away in a river and never found. However, numismatists have agreed that none of the 37 coins found in the mound was minted later than 625, and if the ship burial commemorated Æthelhere, it would have been odd not to bury any later coins. Two spoons with the Latin forms of the names of the converted Christian Saul/Paul engraved on them were found in the ship: but ship burial was a pagan practice). This has confirmed historians' beliefs that the burial commemorated Rædwald, king of East Anglia, who was baptised as a Christian but is known to have reverted to his pagan beliefs later in life and died in 625. It is thought that his body was never buried in the ship, but that the burial was more of a memorial or cenotaph.

The raven on the shield can be linked with Anglo-Saxon and Old Norse poetry which frequently refers to the raven as the bird which devours the flesh of the dead: warriors were often referred to as 'feeder of ravens'.

See also the website:
www.Gettysburg.edu/~s444637/suttonhoo.htm

2 Boldron is from *boli* (bulls) and *rum* (clearing) and means 'a clearing for bulls'.
Garstang comes from *geirr* (spear) and *stong* (post or stake) and is probably the site of a meeting place.
Whitbeck is from *hvitr* (white) and *bekkr* (stream) and means 'white stream'.
Many place names are derived from the names of the people who settled there: for example, Oadby, Leicestershire (Audr's farm) and Claxby, Lincolnshire (Klakkr's farm).

See also:
Mills, A D (1998) *Oxford Dictionary of English Place-Names*. Oxford: Oxford University Press.
Room, A (1992) *Brewer's Dictionary of Names*. London: Cassell.

3 Postcards showing the interiors of Tudor homes are available from the Victoria & Albert Museum, Cromwell Road, South Kensington, London SW7 2RL Tel: 020 7942 200.

4 A useful picture is the portrait of Sir Henry Unton, painted in 1596 by an unknown artist, which is in the National Portrait Galler, London. Scenes of everyday events by Brueghel are also useful because, although their subjects are not usually British, many of them include scores of people.

5 A book which will help with this is:
(2000) *Developing Literacy Text Level Year 4*. London: A & C Black.

6 An evaluation sheet for instructions can be found in:
(2000) *Developing Literacy Text Level Year 3*. London: A & C Black.

7 The pictures in Activity sheet 1 are of places in Wavertree, Liverpool. The picture shows a mounting-block used in the nineteenth century to help churchgoers to get on and off their horses. The steps are thought to be older than this and to have come from an old stile. The origin of the horse-shoe prints is a mystery. Some people say they were put there to commemorate a demolished smithy. Others say that horse-thieves used to be hanged there. The stone is known as the 'Salisbury Stone', named after Lord Salisbury, who had several stones erected to mark the boundaries of a lake (commemorated by Lake Road) which was drained. The octagonal building was a small jail.

Some of these places are also featured in Activity sheet 2: there was a mill on the site of the modern house mentioned. There used to be a well (and a small monastery) in Monkswell Drive. 'Cuffs Bar' is in a former police station: the coat of arms is that of Lancashire.